The

MIRFIELD
MISSION HYMN-BOOK

New Edition (Revised) with Supplement

PUBLISHED BY
THE COMMUNITY OF THE RESURRECTION
MIRFIELD

To be obtained from

THE SECRETARY
HOUSE OF THE RESURRECTION
MIRFIELD, YORKS

PREFACE

THE MIRFIELD MISSION HYMN-BOOK was first published by the Community of the Resurrection in 1907. It has been widely used, not only in Parochial Missions conducted by members of the Community and by other Mission Priests, but also as a supplement to other hymn books in ordinary parochial worship.

In 1922 the book was revised. Some of the old familiar mission hymns which were popular in pre-war days, but had lost their power of appeal in the changed conditions of life, were omitted. Others, which the advancing standards of taste in hymnology would have rejected, but which in the opinion of experienced missioners still retained their old power to elicit and express the devotion of simple folk to our Blessed Lord, were deliberately retained. Thus, whilst retaining all that was good and helpful in the old book, it was possible to add many hymns of the type which the new edition of Hymns A. & M. and the English Hymnal had made popular; and in addition to include a number of new hymns, not previously published, which emphasised the social and sacramental aspects of the Gospel message.

In the present book the words of the 1922 edition remain unaltered, but many of the tunes have been supplemented, or new ones substituted.

We have also added a Supplement of forty-five additional hymns. In doing so we have aimed at supplying some obvious omissions in the old book; and have also tried to provide more adequately for the needs of the Church's Seasons.

We have aimed not at compromise, but at comprehension; we hope to meet the needs of as many different types of people as possible. In the present book we have striven to make provision for the fullest possible expression of devotion to our Blessed Lord and to His Church. Both subjective and objective types of hymn have their due place. The Evangelical assertion of the power of the Cross, and the cleansing of the Precious Blood, lead on to the gifts of Grace which flow from the Risen Life of our Saviour in the fellowship of the Catholic Church.

Our best thanks are due to Mr. Dudley Hill and Mr. Martin Pierce for much valuable help in preparing the music edition. We have again to thank Mr. Herbert H. Fletcher, our Secretary, for invaluable help in preparing the book for the press.

Every effort has been made to ensure that no copyright, either of words or music, should be infringed; and if we have failed in any case, we desire to apologise, and to promise that the omitted acknowledgement shall be inserted at the earliest opportunity.

The following tunes are the copyright of the Community of the Resurrection: 3(2), 14, 15, 32, 35, 68, 86, 89(2), 96, 97, 160, 162, 163, 166, 192, 207, 208, and the following hymns: 14, 15, 32, 35, 42, 86, 160, 187.

The following hymns are inserted by permission of the owners: Nos. 22, 104, Messrs. Ridley & Co.; 70, 93, 152, 185, 189, 190, 193, from the *English Hymnal*, by permission of the Oxford University Press; 180, 204, from the *Yattendon Hymnal*, by permission of the Oxford University Press; 191, from the *English Hymnal*, by permission of Mr. William Galbraith and the Oxford University Press; 153, from the *English Hymnal*, by permission of the Executors of the late Rev. V. S. S. Coles and the Oxford University Press; 192, Messrs. Longmans Green & Co.; 205, Messrs. Burns Oates & Washbourne; 216, The Beacon Press Inc., Boston, Mass.; and we desire to express our gratitude to them and to the following owners of copyright who have kindly granted the use of hymns or tunes :—The Proprietors of the following hymn books : *The Congregational Hymnary, Hymns Ancient and Modern, The Public School Hymn Book*, Messrs. Cary & Co., Messrs. Gwenlyn Evans & Son, Messrs. Hughes & Son, Messrs. Marshall, Morgan & Scott, Messrs. Nisbet & Co., Messrs. Novello & Co., Messrs. Stainer & Bell, Mrs. T. Adams, Hon. Rev. J. G. Adderley, Canon W. Hay Aitken, Miss Amps, the Rev. Fr. Andrew, Rev. A. H. Baverstock, Rev. Dr. Bickersteth, Mr. L. Body, Dr. P. C. Buck, Capt. F. Burgess, Lady Carbery, Rev. V. S. S. Coles, Miss Dodson, Rev. Canon Dugmore, Rev. W. H. Ferguson, Dr. Basil Harwood, Miss B. Hatch, Deaconess Hensley, Mr. G. von Holst, Miss Morley Horder, the Ven. Archdeacon How, the Warden of Keble, Mrs. Latter Parsons, Rev. Canon Lester, the Lord Bishop of Llandaff, Rev. S. C. Lowry, Mr. E. Maclagan, Mr. Peter Martineau, Miss Matheson, Miss Maude, Mrs. Midlane, Mr. L. B. C. Muirhead, Mrs. Munro, Dr. E. W. Naylor, Dr. S. H. Nicholson, Miss P. Otway, Rev. E. S. Palmer, Mrs. Palmer, Mrs. Pennyfather, Lt.-Col. Pollock, Miss A. E. Rashdall, Rev. Canon Ross, Royal College of Music, Ven. Archdeacon Scott, Dr. Geoffrey Shaw, Rev. A. H. Havergal Shaw, Rev. J. Stephens, Dr. Eugene Stock, Rev. Fr. Superior, Mount St. Bernard's Abbey, Coalville, Rev. Canon Swire, Lt.-Col. Turton, Mrs. Taylor, Mrs. Walch, Dr. Walford Davies, Rev. Claude Williams.

NOTE.—As far as possible the name of the author and composer is given with each hymn and tune, together with the date of the first publication. When the latter is not known the date of his birth and death (if not still living) is given.

In this revised edition (1936) a number of small corrections have been made and the general appearance and utility of the book have been improved by new type for many tunes and a rearrangement of the pages.

D. J. H.
M. P.

FORM OF SERVICE FOR THE RECEPTION OF THE MISSIONERS

The Clergy and Choir having taken their places, there shall be silence for a space, during which the accustomed devotions may be said silently. Then the Officiant shall say at his place in the Sanctuary :

℣. O God, make speed to save us.
℟. O Lord, make haste to help us.
℣. Glory be to the FATHER, and to the SON : and to the HOLY GHOST.
℟. As it was in the beginning, is now, and ever shall be : world without end. Amen.
ALL SAY : Alleluia.

From Septuagesima to Easter, instead of "Alleluia" say:
O King of endless glory,
Praise be to Thee for evermore.

ANTIPHON : All that the Father hath given Me shall come to Me.

PSALM 111

1. I will give thanks unto the Lord with my whole heart : secretly among the faithful, and in the congregation.

2. The works of the Lord are great : sought out of all them that have pleasure therein.

3. His work is worthy to be praised, and had in honour : and his righteousness endureth for ever.

4. The merciful and gracious Lord hath so done his marvellous works : that they ought to be had in remembrance.

5. He hath given meat unto them that fear him : he shall ever be mindful of his covenant.

6. He hath shewed his people the power of his works : that he may give them the heritage of the heathen.

7. The works of his hands are verity and judgment : all his commandments are true.

8. They stand fast for ever and ever : and are done in truth and equity.

9. He sent redemption unto his people : he hath commanded his covenant for ever, holy and reverend is his Name.

10. The fear of the Lord is the beginning of wisdom : a good understanding have all they that do thereafter; the praise of it endureth for ever.

Glory be to the FATHER, and to the SON ; and to the HOLY GHOST.
As it was in the beginning, is now, and ever shall be : world without end. Amen.

ANTIPHON : All that the Father hath given Me shall come to Me : and him that cometh unto Me, I will in no wise cast out.

The Chapter

S. Luke 5, vv. 1-11 : And it came to pass . . . they forsook all and followed Him.

Office Hymn

Come, Thou Holy Spirit, come . . . (No. 19).

ANTIPHON : Master, we have toiled all the night, and have taken nothing.

Magnificat (No. 174)

My soul doth magnify the Lord, etc.

ANTIPHON : Master, we have toiled all the night, and have taken nothing : nevertheless at Thy word I will let down the net.

℣. The Lord be with you.

℟. And with thy spirit.

Let us Pray

GOD, Who didst teach the hearts of Thy faithful people, by the sending to them the light of Thy Holy Spirit ; Grant us by the same Spirit to have a right judgment in all things, and evermore to rejoice in His holy comfort ; through the merits of Christ Jesus our Saviour, Who liveth and reigneth with Thee, in the unity of the same Spirit, one God, world without end. Amen.

℣. The Lord be with you.

℟. And with thy spirit.

℣. Let us bless the Lord.

℟. Thanks be to God.

℣. May the souls of the faithful, through the mercy of God, rest in peace.

℟. Amen.

A hymn to the Holy Spirit may be sung here. Nos. 13 or 182 are suitable.
During the singing of the hymn the Missioners (conducted by the Church-wardens) advance to the entrance to the Choir. The Parish Priest (or Bishop, if he be present) advances to the chancel gates, and there addresses the Missioners after this sort:

REVEREND FATHERS, we have heard in the Chapter the words of our Saviour Christ, Who also hath taught us by His holy Apostle that our heavenly Father willeth all men to be saved and come to the knowledge of the truth.

We therefore bid you welcome to this church and parish to preach the Word, for the strengthening of such as do stand, for the comfort of the weak-hearted, and for the raising up of those who have fallen ; praying also that many souls may be added to the Lord.

Be assured that we have looked for your coming with prayer and supplication, and by the pleading of the most Holy Sacrifice of the Body and Blood of Christ.

And now with the consent and blessing of . . . our Bishop (who has himself commended your labours by a letter to the people of this place), I commit to you the charge of this Mission, in the name of our Lord Jesus Christ (relying on the merits and prayers of Saint . . . patron of this church, together with those of Blessed Mary and all the Saints) praying that you may receive every grace and blessing, and that through you many may be turned to righteousness, and shine as the stars for ever and ever.

Then shall he bless the Missioners, saying:

GOD the FATHER, GOD the SON, and GOD the HOLY GHOST bless, guide and strengthen you now and for evermore. Amen.

After the Blessing the Parish Priest shall conduct the Missioners to their places in the Choir.
A hymn shall here be sung, after which an Address shall be given by the Bishop (or one of the Missioners).
A hymn may now be sung, after which the Blessing shall be given by the Bishop (or the senior Missioner).

When the Reception of the Missioners takes place at the Holy Eucharist, before the service, or at the conclusion of the Nicene Creed, the Missioners are escorted by the Churchwardens to the entrance of the Chancel.
Kneeling at some convenient place, they are addressed by the Parish Priest (or by the Bishop, if he be present) as above:

REVEREND FATHERS, we have heard, etc.

PRAYERS FOR THE MISSION

O LORD, without Whom our labour is lost, and with Whom Thy little ones go forth as the mighty ; revive Thy work in the coming Mission by a rich outpouring of the HOLY SPIRIT in love and power and converting grace, and grant to Thy labourers a pure intention, patient faith, sufficient success upon earth and the bliss of serving Thee in heaven ; through JESUS CHRIST our LORD. AMEN.

O GOD, bless the Mission to my soul, and to the souls of many more, and use us in Thy service, for JESUS CHRIST'S sake. AMEN.

Our FATHER, which art in heaven, Hallowed be Thy Name ; Thy kingdom come ; Thy will be done ; In earth as it is in heaven. Give us this day our daily bread. And forgive us our trespasses, As we forgive them that trespass against us. And lead us not into temptation ; But deliver us from evil. AMEN.

1

MILES LANE.   C.M.   W. SHRUBSOLE, 1779.

crown Him, crown Him, crown Him, crown Him Lord of all.

(Or 220, Second Tune.)

ALL hail the power of JESUS' Name ;
  Let Angels prostrate fall ;
Bring forth the royal diadem
  And crown Him LORD of all.

Crown Him, ye morning stars of light,
  Who fix'd this floating ball ;
Now hail the Strength of Israel's might
  And crown Him LORD of all.

Crown Him, ye Martyrs of your GOD,
  Who from His Altar call ;
Extol the Stem-of-Jesse's Rod,
  And crown Him LORD of all.

Ye seed of Israel's chosen race,
  Ye ransom'd of the fall,
Hail Him Who saves you by His grace,
  And crown Him LORD of all.

Hail Him, ye heirs of David's line,
  Whom David LORD did call,
The GOD Incarnate, Man Divine,
  And crown Him LORD of all.

Sinners, whose love can ne'er forget
  The wormwood and the gall,
Go spread your trophies at His Feet,
  And crown Him LORD of all.

Let every tribe and every tongue
  Before Him prostrate fall,
And shout in universal song
  The crownèd LORD of all.

E. PERRONETT, 1780.

2

2

Nicht So Traurig.   7.7.7.7.7.7.   J. S. Bach, 1685-1750.
Slow and dignified.

All my sins uprising now,
  Wring my heart and brand my brow;
Sins of childhood, sins of youth,
  Despite done to Grace and Truth:
Is there mercy left for me?—
  Jesus died! He died for thee.

Deeds and words and fancies vain,
  Darker, deadlier made the stain
On the record kept on high,
  On my soul condemned to die:
Is there cleansing left for me?—
  Jesus bled! He bled for thee.

Ah! my heart is hard within,
  Callous through repeated sin;
When I fain would kneel and pray
  Satan steals the power away;
Say, what hope remains for me?—
  Jesus prayed! He prays for thee.

Once, far back in earlier years,
  I bedewed my couch with tears;
Now no gracious drops will flow
  From the deeper fount of woe;
Death and Judgement wait for me;
  Jesus wept! He wept for thee.

Dare I lift my shameful face—
  I who trampled on His Grace?
Dare I seek the Throne of light,
  Where His saints are clad in white?
How they all would shrink from me!—
  Jesus bends! He bends to thee.

Jesus died, to make thee whole;
  Jesus bled; to wash thy soul;
Jesus prayed; and thou hast part!
  Jesus wept; to break thy heart;
Jesus bends! poor sinner, see!
  Rise! Look up! He calleth thee!

G. S. Hodges, 1875.

3

SHIPSTON.
(First Tune.)
8.7.8.7.
English Traditional Melody.

(From the English Hymnal, by permission of the Oxford University Press.)

I

ALL we have we owe to JESUS,
  His dear children all are we ;
Through all troubles He will bring us
  His bright home in Heaven to see.

With the FATHER and the SPIRIT,
  He is ever GOD the SON ;
There was never a beginning
  To the Holy Three in One.

Once He laid aside His glory,
  And was born a little child,
Of the Blessed Virgin Mary—
  Maiden meek, and Mother mild.

Thirty years in secret dwelling,
  He fulfilled His FATHER'S Will,
And for three years showed His glory,
  Patient and obedient still.

Then He blessed the little children,
  And His mighty works He wrought ;
And He taught His true disciples
  How to serve Him as they ought.

Then He let the wicked traitor
  Sell Him to His cruel foes ;
Let the soldiers strip and scourge Him,
  For our sakes, with bitter blows.

On the Cross they nailed His Body,
  And they set Him up on high ;
Thus the GOD of earth and heaven
  For our sins did truly die.

From the Cross His Blood was streaming,
  All our sins to wash away ;
In that Precious Blood He washed us
  On our bright, baptismal day.

Cleansed from sin, His FATHER'S children
  And His members we became,
Gifts of faith and grace receiving
  Through the power of His dear Name.

4

3

ROSETTENVILLE.
(Second Tune.)

8.7.8.7.

G. W. HART, C.R., 1902.

II

Now dear JESUS reigns in Heaven,
  Yet is with us here below ;
Smiles upon us when we please Him,
  Sorrows when astray we go.

Therefore we must give Him gladly
  Every action, thought and word ;
And His loving voice of warning
  Must within our hearts be heard.

If the devil should persuade us
  Our dear LORD to disobey,
Very earnestly to JESUS
  For His pardon we must pray.

He will give it if we ask Him,
  And if still our hearts are sad,
Words of Holy Absolution
  From His Priest shall make us glad.

Greater things He yet will give us,
  For our LORD is very good ;
He will give us at His Altar
  His own Body and His Blood.

When to satisfy our longing
  Will that happy day arrive ?
That we may be ready for it,
  Daily, daily, let us strive.

First in Holy Confirmation
  We the sevenfold gifts must share
Of the HOLY GHOST descending
  On us at the Bishop's prayer.

Then may we receive our Saviour,
  Taste His sweetness, and His love
Feed on Him in faith adoring,
  Till we reign with Him above.

All we have we owe to JESUS,
  His dear children all are we,
Through all troubles He will bring us
  His bright home in Heaven to see.

V. S. S. COLES (1845—1929).

5

4

ALLELUIA ! sing to JESUS !
His the Sceptre, His the Throne ;
Alleluia ! His the triumph,
His the victory alone ;
Hark ! the songs of peaceful Sion
Thunder like a mighty flood ;
JESUS out of every nation
Hath redeem'd us by His Blood.

Alleluia ! not as orphans
Are we left in sorrow now ;
Alleluia ! He is near us,
Faith believes, nor questions how ;
Though the cloud from sight received Him,
When the forty days were o'er,
Shall our hearts forget His promise,
" I am with you evermore " ?

Alleluia ! Bread of Angels,
Thou on earth our Food, our Stay ;
Alleluia ! here the sinful
Flee to Thee from day to day ;
Intercessor, Friend of sinners,
Earth's Redeemer, plead for me,
Where the songs of all the sinless
Sweep across the crystal sea.

Alleluia ! King Eternal,
Thee the LORD of lords we own ;
Alleluia ! born of Mary,
Earth Thy footstool, Heav'n Thy throne
Thou within the veil hast enter'd,
Robed in flesh, our great High Priest ;
Thou on earth both Priest and Victim
In the Eucharistic Feast.

Alleluia ! sing to JESUS !
His the Sceptre, His the Throne ;
Alleluia ! His the triumph,
His the victory alone ;
Hark ! the songs of peaceful Sion
Thunder like a mighty flood ;
JESUS out of every nation
Hath redeem'd us by His Blood.

W. C. DIX, 1866.

5

ALMIGHTY GOD, Whose only SON
O'er sin and death the triumph won,
And ever lives to intercede
For souls, who Thy sweet mercy need;

In His dear Name to Thee we pray
For all who err and go astray,
For sinners, wheresoe'er they be,
Who do not serve and honour Thee.

There are who never yet have heard
The tidings of Thy blessèd Word,
But still in heathen darkness dwell,
Without one thought of heaven or hell;

And some within Thy sacred fold
To holy things are dead and cold,
And waste the precious hours of life
In selfish ease, or toil, or strife;

And many a quicken'd soul within
There lurks the secret love of sin,
A wayward will, or anxious fears,
Or lingering taint of bygone years.

O give repentance, true and deep,
To all Thy lost and wandering sheep,
And kindle in their hearts the fire
Of holy love and pure desire.

That so from Angel hosts above,
May rise a sweeter song of love,
And we, with all the Blest, adore
Thy Name, O GOD, for evermore.

H. W. BAKER, 1868.

6

UNDE ET MEMORES.   10.10.10.10.10.10.   W. H. MONK, 1875.

(By permission of the Proprietors of Hymns A. & M.)

AND now, O FATHER, mindful of the love
  That bought us, once for all, on Calvary's
      Tree,
And having with us Him That pleads
    above,
  We here present, we here spread forth
    to Thee
That only Offering perfect in Thine
    Eyes,
The one true, pure, immortal Sacrifice.

Look, FATHER, look on His anointed
    Face,
  And only look on us as found in Him;
Look not on our misusings of Thy Grace,
  Our prayer so languid and our faith so
    dim;
For lo! between our sins and their re-
    ward
We set the Passion of Thy SON our LORD.

And then for those, our dearest and our
    best,
  By this prevailing Presence we appeal;
O fold them closer to Thy mercy's breast,
  O do Thine utmost for their souls' true
    weal;
From tainting mischief keep them white
    and clear,
And crown Thy gifts with strength to
    persevere.

And so we come; O draw us to Thy Feet,
  Most patient SAVIOUR, Who canst love
    us still;
And by this Food, so awful and so sweet,
  Deliver us from every touch of ill:
In Thine own service make us glad and
    free,
And grant us never more to part with
    Thee.

W. BRIGHT, 1873.

7

ART THOU WEARY. 8.5.8.3. P. OTWAY.

(Or Tune 47.)

ART thou weary, art thou languid,
  Art thou sore distrest?
" Come to Me," saith One, " and coming
      Be at rest ! "

Hath He marks to lead me to Him,
  If He be my Guide?
" In His Feet and Hands are wound-prints,
      And His Side."

Hath He diadem as monarch
  That His Brow adorns?
" Yea, a crown, in very surety,
      But of thorns."

If I find Him, if I follow,
  What His guerdon here?
" Many a sorrow, many a labour,
      Many a tear."

If I still hold closely to Him,
  What hath He at last?
" Sorrow vanquished, labour ended,
      Jordan past."

If I ask Him to receive me,
  Will He say me nay?
" Not till earth, and not till Heaven
      Pass away."

Finding, following, keeping, struggling,
  Is He sure to bless?
" Angels, Martyrs, Prophets, Virgins,
      Answer, Yes ! "

J. M. NEALE, 1862.

8

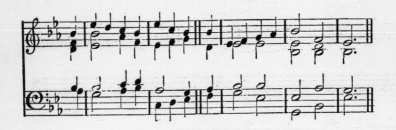

(Or A.M. 335.)

AROUND the throne of GOD a band
Of glorious Angels always stand ;
Bright things they see, sweet harps they hold,
And on their heads are crowns of gold.

Some wait around Him, ready still
To sing His praise and do His will ;
And some, when He commands them, go
To guard His servants here below.

LORD, give Thine Angels every day
Command to guide us on our way,
And bid them every evening keep
Their watch around us while we sleep.

So shall no wicked thing draw near,
To do us harm or cause us fear ;
And we shall dwell, when life is past,
With Angels round Thy throne at last.

J. M. NEALE, 1843.

9

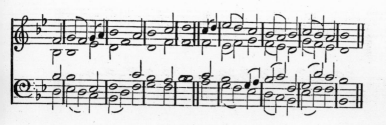

ASHAMED of Thee ! O dearest LORD,
 I marvel how such wrong can be ;
And yet how oft in deed and word
 Have I been found ashamed of Thee !

Ashamed of Thee ! My King, my GOD,
 Who soughtest me with wondrous love,
Whose Feet the way of sorrows trod
 To bring me to Thy home above ;

Ashamed of Thee !—of that blest Name
 Which speaks of mercy full and free ;
Nay, LORD, be this my only shame,
 That I have been ashamed of Thee.

Ashamed of Thee ! Whose love divine
 Was not ashamed of our lost race ;
But even this cold heart of mine
 Doth make Thy home and dwelling-place.

Ashamed of Thee ! O LORD, I pray
 This cruel wrong no more may be ;
And in Thy last great Advent-day
 Oh, be not Thou ashamed of me !

                    W. WALSHAM HOW, 1882.

10

ANGELUS.   L.M.   G. JOSEPH, 1657.

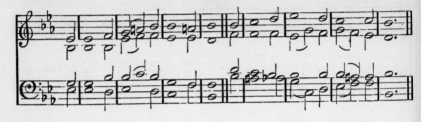

AT even, ere the sun was set,
The sick, O LORD, around Thee lay ;
Oh, in what divers pains they met !
Oh, with what joy they went away !

Once more 'tis eventide, and we
Oppress'd with various ills draw near :
What if Thy Form we cannot see ?
We know and feel that Thou art here.

O SAVIOUR CHRIST, our woes dispel ;
For some are sick, and some are sad,
And some have never loved Thee well,
And some have lost the love they had ;

And some have found the world is vain,
Yet from the world they break not free ;
And some have friends who give them pain,
Yet have not sought a friend in Thee ;

And none, O LORD, have perfect rest,
For none are wholly free from sin ;
And they, who fain would serve Thee best,
Are conscious most of wrong within.

O SAVIOUR CHRIST, Thou too art Man ;
Thou hast been troubled, tempted, tried ;
Thy kind but searching glance can scan
The very wounds that shame would hide ;

Thy touch hath still its ancient power ;
No word from Thee can fruitless fall ;
Hear, in this solemn evening hour,
And in Thy mercy heal us all.

H. TWELLS, 1868.

11

Ave Maria ! blessèd Maid!
Lily of Eden's fragrant shade !
　Who can express the love
That nurtured thee, so pure and sweet,
Making thy heart a shelter meet
　For Jesus' holy Dove !

Ave Maria ! Mother blest,
To whom, caressing and caressed,
　Clings the eternal Child ;
Favoured beyond Archangels' dream,
When first on thee with tenderest gleam
　Thy new-born Saviour smiled.

Thou wept'st, meek Maiden, Mother mild,
Thou wept'st upon thy sinless Child,
　Thy very heart was riven :
And yet what mourning matron here
Would deem thy sorrows bought too dear
　By all on this side Heaven !

A Son that never did amiss,
That never shamed His Mother's kiss,
　Nor crossed her fondest prayer :
E'en from the Tree He deign'd to bow
For her His agonizèd Brow,
　Her, His sole earthly care.

Ave Maria ! thou whose name
All but adoring love may claim,
　Yet may we reach thy shrine ;
For He, thy Son and Saviour, vows
To crown all lowly, lofty brows
　With love and joy like thine.

J. Keble, 1827.

12

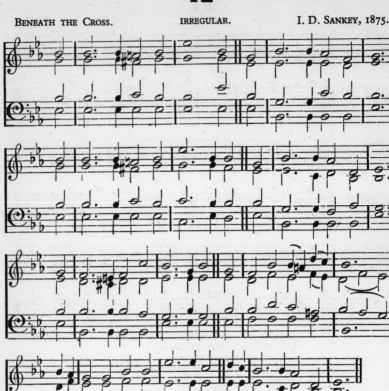

(By permission of Morgan & Scott Ltd.)

BENEATH the Cross of JESUS
   I fain would take my stand—
The shadow of a mighty Rock,
   Within a weary land.
A home within the wilderness,
   A rest upon the way,
From the burning of the noontide heat,
   And the burden of the day.

O safe and happy shelter !
   O refuge tried and sweet!
O trysting-place where Heaven's love
   And Heaven's justice meet.
As to the holy Patriarch
   That wondrous dream was given,
So seems my SAVIOUR's Cross to me—
   A ladder up to Heaven.

There lies beneath its shadow,
   But on the further side,
The darkness of an awful grave
   That gapes both deep and wide ;

And there between us stands the Cross,
   Two arms outstretched to save,
Like a watchman set to guard the way
   From that eternal grave.

Upon that Cross of JESUS
   Mine eye at times can see
The very dying form of One
   Who suffered there for me ;
And from my smitten heart with tears,
   Two wonders I confess—
The wonders of His glorious love,
   And my own worthlessness.

I take, O Cross, thy shadow,
   For my abiding place ;
I ask no other sunshine
   Than the sunshine of His Face ;
Content to let the world go by,
   To know no gain nor loss,
My sinful self my only shame,
   My glory all—the Cross.

             E. C. CLEPHANE, 1872.

TRENTHAM. S.M. R. JACKSON, 1894.

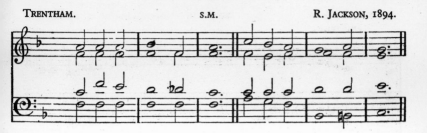

(Or 123, First Tune.)

BREATHE on me, Breath of GOD,
　　Fill me with life anew,
That I may love what Thou dost love,
　　And do what Thou would'st do.

　　Breathe on me, Breath of GOD,
　　　　Until my heart is pure ;
Until with Thee I will one will
　　　　To do and to endure.

　　　Breathe on me, Breath of GOD,
　　　　　Till I am wholly Thine ;
　Until this earthly part of me
　　　　　Glows with Thy fire divine.

　　　Breathe on me, Breath of GOD,
　　　　　So shall I never die,
　But live with Thee the perfect life
　　　　　Of Thine eternity.

　　　　　　　　　E. HATCH, 1878.

14

BALLO DI MANOVA.　　　　IRREGULAR.　　Arr. by Bp. W. H. Frere, C.R.
In Unison.

I

CHRIST from Heaven descended; the SON OF GOD
    most holy
Stooped to our nature, and lived a servant lowly;
In our human nature, and for the world's salvation
Torments He suffered, and anguish of temptation.
Men and fiends assailed Him,
His own disciples failed Him.
Yet He bore His Manhood unscathed in full perfec-
    tion
Through Cross and Passion to glorious Resurrection.

CHRIST the world's Redeemer, His FATHER's love
    revealing,
Wrought mighty wonders of mercy and of healing;
Outcasts lone and sinners He drew with love most
    tender
To life and freedom and joy of self-surrender.
Still His message ringeth,
Abounding hope it bringeth—
Come to Me, ye weary, rest for your souls I give you,
Come, heavy laden, your sins I will forgive you.

II

CHRIST for ever liveth in light for ever glorious;
CHRIST ever reigneth o'er every foe victorious;
CHRIST in highest glory His Manhood ever weareth,
Now on His Bosom His brethren's names He beareth;
Opened are Heaven's portals
To all earth's ransomed mortals;
CHRIST for ever pleadeth with ceaseless intercession
His perfect offering that covers man's transgression.

Thou, O CHRIST, hast triumphed, and in Thy Church
    Thou livest;
Life to her members, eternal life, Thou givest;
Take, O King of Glory, take now Thy sceptre royal,
Reign Thou unchallenged in humble hearts and loyal;
No mischance can sever
Thine own from Thee for ever;
Praises unto Thee, LORD, Thy Church is aye address-
    ing—
Thine be for ever the glory and the blessing.

                        T. REES, C.R., 1922.

15

ST. DEINIOL.   D.C.M. and Refrain.   S. H. NICHOLSON, 1922.

In Unison.   *(First Tune.)*

REFRAIN.

18

15

(From the English Hymnal, by permission of the Oxford University Press.)

CHRIST is the Sacrifice we plead
Before th' eternal Throne ;
His Cross alone can cancel guilt
And for our sins atone.
We shelter 'neath that sacrifice
In every hour of need ;
And at the Altar bending low
That Sacrifice we plead.

CHRIST is the heavenly Food that gives
To every famished soul
New life and strength, new joy and hope,
And faith that maketh whole.
For we are made for GOD alone,
Without Him we are dead ;
No food sufficeth for the soul
But CHRIST the Living Bread.

Beneath the veil of bread and wine
Our LORD Who reigns above
Is present as our Sacrifice ;
O praise His wondrous love.

Beneath the veil of bread and wine
Our LORD Who reigns above
Is present as our Heavenly Food ;
O praise His wondrous love.

CHRIST is the Unity that binds
In one the near and far ;
For we who share His life divine
His living body are.
On earth and in the realms beyond,
One fellowship are we ;
And at the Altar we are knit
In mystic unity.

Beneath the veil of bread and wine
Our LORD Who reigns above
Is present as our Unity ;
O praise His wondrous love.

T. REES, 1922.

16

SOLDIERS OF THE CHURCH.   8.7.8.7.D. and Refrain.   T. MORLEY.

In Unison.

CHRISTIANS, sing the Incarnation
  Of th' Eternal SON of GOD,
Who, to save us, took our nature,
  Soul and body, flesh and blood :
GOD, He saw man's cruel bondage,
  Who in death's dark dungeon lay ;
MAN, He came to fight man's battle,
  And for man He won the day.
    Alleluia, Alleluia
      To th' Incarnate SON of GOD,
      Who for man as Man hath conquer'd
      In our own true flesh and blood.

King of kings and Lord of Angels,
  He puts off His glory-crown,
Had a stable-cave for palace,
  And a manger for His throne ;
Helpless lay, to Whom creation
  All its life and being owed,
And the lowly Hebrew Maiden
  Was the Mother of her GOD.
    Alleluia, Alleluia
      To th' Incarnate SON of GOD,
      Who conceal d His dazzling GODHEAD
      'Neath the veil of flesh and blood.

Through a life of lowly labour
  He on earth was pleased to dwell,
All our want and sorrow sharing,
  GOD with us, EMMANUEL :
Yet a dearer, closer union
  JESUS in His love would frame ;
He, the Passover fulfilling,
  Gave Himself as Paschal Lamb.
    Alleluia, Alleluia
      To th' Incarnate SON of GOD,
      Who the heav'nly gifts bequeath'd us
      Of His own true Flesh and Blood.

Then, by man refused and hated,
  GOD for man vouchsafed to die,
Love divine its depth revealing
  On the heights of Calvary ;
Through His dying the dominion
  From the tyrant death was torn,
When its Victim rose its Victor
  On the Resurrection morn.
    Alleluia, Alleluia
      To th' Incarnate SON of GOD,
      Who through His eternal SPIRIT
      Offers His own Flesh and Blood.

Forty days of mystic converse
  Lived on earth the Risen One,
Speaking of His earthly kingdom,
  Ere He sought His heav'nly Throne :
Then, His latest words a blessing,
  He ascended up on high,
And through rank on rank of Angels
  Captive led captivity.
    Alleluia, Alleluia
      To th' Incarnate SON of GOD,
      Who the Holiest place hath enter'd
      In our flesh and by His Blood.

Now upon the golden Altar,
  In the midst before the Throne,
Incense of His intercession
  He is offering for His own ;
And on earth at all His altars
  His true Presence we adore,
And His Sacrifice is pleaded,
  Yea, till time shall be no more.
    Alleluia, Alleluia
      To th' Incarnate SON of GOD,
      Who, abiding Priest for ever,
      Still imparts His Flesh and Blood.

Then, adored in highest Heaven,
  We shall see the Virgin's Son,
All creation bow'd before Him,
  MAN upon the eternal Throne :
Where, like sound of many waters
  In one ever rising flood,
Myriad voices hymn His triumph,
  Victim, Priest, Incarnate GOD.
    Worthy He all praise and blessing
      Who, by dying, death o'ercame :
    Glory be to GOD for ever !
    Alleluia to the LAMB !

                              E. DUGMORE, 1878.

17

VENI CREATOR.
In free rhythm. In Unison.

L.M. *Melody from " Vesperale Romanum "*
(Mechlin).

Final lines

Praise___ to thy e — ter — nal merit, Fa — ther, Son, and Ho — ly Spirit. A — men.

COME, HOLY GHOST, our souls inspire,
And lighten with celestial fire;
Thou the anointing SPIRIT art,
Who dost Thy sevenfold gifts impart.

Thy blessèd unction from above
Is comfort, life and fire of love;
Enable with perpetual light
The dullness of our blinded sight.

Anoint and cheer our soilèd face
With the abundance of Thy grace;
Keep far our foes, give peace at home,
Where Thou art Guide no ill can come.

Teach us to know the FATHER, SON,
And THEE, of Both, to be but ONE;
That through the ages all along
This may be our endless song.
    Praise to Thine eternal merit,
    FATHER, SON and HOLY SPIRIT.

Tr. J. COSIN, 1627.

18

WARRINGTON.   L.M.   R. HARRISON, 1784.

COME, let us sing the Song of songs;
  The Saints in Heaven began the strain,
The homage which to CHRIST belongs;
  Worthy the LAMB, for He was slain.

Slain to redeem us by His Blood,
  To cleanse from every sinful stain,
And make us kings and priests to GOD:
  Worthy the LAMB, for He was slain.

To Him Who suffered on the tree,
  Our souls at His soul's price to gain,
Blessing and praise and glory be:
  Worthy the LAMB, for He was slain.

To Him, enthroned by filial right,
  All power, in Heaven and earth proclaim,
Honour, and majesty, and might:
  Worthy the LAMB, for He was slain.

Long as we live, and when we die,
  And while in Heaven with Him we reign,
This song our Song of songs shall be:
  Worthy the LAMB, for He was slain.

J. MONTGOMERY.

23

19

VENI SANCTE SPIRITUS.　　　　7.7.7.D.　　　S. WEBBE the elder, 1740-1816.

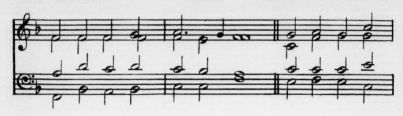

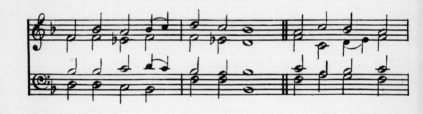

COME, Thou HOLY SPIRIT, come;
And from Thy celestial home
   Shed a ray of light Divine;
Come, Thou FATHER of the poor,
Come, Thou source of all our store,
   Come, within our bosoms shine.

Thou of comforters the best,
Thou the soul's most welcome Guest,
   Sweet refreshment here below;
In our labour rest most sweet,
Grateful coolness in the heat,
   Solace in the midst of woe.

O most blessèd Light Divine,
Shine within these hearts of Thine,
   And our inmost being fill;
Where Thou art not, man hath nought,
Nothing good in deed or thought,
   Nothing free from taint of ill.

Heal our wounds; our strength renew.
On our dryness pour Thy dew;
   Wash the stains of guilt away:
Bend the stubborn heart and will;
Melt the frozen, warm the chill;
   Guide the steps that go astray.

On the faithful, who adore
And confess Thee, evermore
   In Thy sevenfold Gifts descend
Give them virtue's sure reward;
Give them Thy salvation, LORD;
   Give them joys that never end.

Tr. E. CASWALL, 1847.

MANNHEIM.   8.7.8.7.8.7.   *Altered from Chorale by* F. FILITZ, 1804-1876.

COME, ye sinners, poor and needy,
   Come in mercy's gracious hour ;
JESUS ready stands to save you,
   Full of pity, love and power.
He is able, He is willing ; doubt no more !

Come, ye needy, come and welcome,
   GOD's free bounty glorify :
True belief and true repentance,
   Every grace that brings us nigh,
Without money come to JESUS CHRIST and buy !

Come, ye weary, heavy-laden,
   Lost and ruined by the Fall ;
If you tarry till you're better,
   You will never come at all :
Not the righteous ; sinners JESUS came to call.

Let not conscience make you linger,
   Nor of fitness fondly dream ;
All the fitness He requireth
   Is to feel your need of Him :
This He gives you ; 'tis the SPIRIT's rising b

Agonizing in the garden,
   Lo ! the SAVIOUR prostrate lies ;
On the bloodstained Cross behold Him,
   Hear Him cry before He dies—
" It is finished ! "—finished the great sacri

Lo ! th' Incarnate GOD, ascended,
   Pleads the merits of His Blood ;
Venture on Him, venture wholly,
   Let no other trust intrude ;
None but JESUS can do helpless sinners go

Saints and Angels, joined in concert,
   Sing the praises of the LAMB :
While the blissful seats of Heaven
   Sweetly echo with His Name :
Alleluia ! sinners here may sing the same.

J. HART, 1759.

N.B.—*The first four syllables of the last line are
repeated in each verse.*

21

(By permission of Novello and Co., Ltd.)

(Or Tune 39.)

Cᴏᴍᴇ ye yourselves apart and rest awhile ;
  Weary, I know it, of the press and throng,
Wipe from your brow the sweat and dust of toil,
  And in My quiet strength again be strong.

Come ye aside from all the world holds dear,
  For converse which the world has never known,
Alone with Me, and with Mʏ Fᴀᴛʜᴇʀ here,
  With Me and with Mʏ Fᴀᴛʜᴇʀ not alone.

Come, tell Me all that ye have said and done,
  Your victories and failures, hopes and fears ;
I know how hardly souls are wooed and won :
  My choicest wreaths are always wet with tears.

Come ye and rest : the journey is too great,
  And ye will faint beside the way and sink ;
The Bread of Life is here for you to eat,
  And here for you the Wine of Love to drink.

Then, fresh from converse with your Lᴏʀᴅ, return
  And work till daylight softens into even ;
The brief hours are not lost in which ye learn
  More of your Mᴀꜱᴛᴇʀ and His rest in Heaven.

E. H. Bɪᴄᴋᴇʀꜱᴛᴇᴛʜ, 1872.

22

REFRAIN.

DAILY, daily sing the praises
  Of the City GOD hath made ;
In the beauteous fields of Eden
  Its foundation-stones are laid ;

Oh, that I had wings of Angels
  Here to spread and heavenward fly:
I would seek the gates of Sion,
  Far beyond the starry sky!

All the walls of that dear City
  Are of bright and burnished gold ;
It is matchless in its beauty,
  And its treasures are untold.

In the midst of that dear City
  CHRIST is reigning on His seat,

And the Angels swing their censers
  In a ring about His Feet.

From the throne a river issues,
  Clear as crystal, passing bright,
And it traverses the City,
  Like a beam of silver light.

There the wind is sweetly fragrant,
  And is laden with the song
Of the Seraphs, and the Elders,
  And the great redeemèd throng.

Oh, I would my ears were open
  Here to catch that happy strain !
Oh, I would my eyes some vision
  Of that Eden could attain !

             S. BARING GOULD, 1867.

Nun Komm.

7.7.7.7.

*Melody in Walther's
'Gesangbuchlein' 1524
Adapted by* J. S. Bach.

Depth of mercy ! can there be
Mercy still reserved for me ?
Can my God His wrath forbear ?—
Me, the chief of sinners, spare ?

I have long withstood His Grace,
Long provoked Him to His Face,
Would not hearken to His calls,
Grieved Him by a thousand falls.

There for me the Saviour stands ;
Shows His wounds and spreads His Hands !
God is love ! I know, I feel ;
Jesus weeps, and loves me still.

Jesus, answer from above,
Is not all Thy nature love ?
Wilt Thou not the wrong forget,
Suffer me to kiss Thy Feet ?

If I rightly read Thy Heart,
If Thou all compassion art,
Bow Thine ear, in mercy bow,
Pardon and accept me now.

C. Wesley, 1745.

24

FAITHFUL warriors, bearing
JESUS' cross and shame;
Faithful warriors, daring
All in JESUS' Name.

Hard the path and dreary
In a world of sin;
Hard the fight and weary
With the lusts within.

Hark! the Voice that calls you
"Warriors, follow Me;
All that now befalls you
Shall your glory be."

On through strife and sorrow
Force your steadfast way:
Bright shall be to-morrow
After dark to-day.

There are holier treasures
Than the world can give;
There are lasting pleasures
Where the Angels live.

There are those that love you
In that happy land:
Round you and above you
Flocks the heavenly band.

Angels lift glad voices
As you draw more near ;
GOD Himself rejoices
When you persevere.

GOD will never leave you
Till your work is done ;
GOD will not deceive you
When the prize is won.

On His word relying,
True and steadfast be ;
Every foe defying,
March to victory.

T. B. POLLOCK, 1836-1896.
*If the tune " Victors " is used, the first verse is
repeated at the end.*

VICTORS.
(Second Tune.)
Unison.

24

6.5.6.5.D.

P. S. JACQUES.

25

8.8.8.8.8.8.

Easy Hymn Tunes, 1851.

FATHER, Who dost Thy children feed
  With Manna rainèd from above ;
Who dost the saving Chalice give,
  Filled by Thy Hand in wondrous love :
We praise Thee for Thy mercies sent
To us in this great Sacrament.

O Word-made-Flesh, Whom we adore,
  The Living Bread sent down from Heaven,
Whose wondrous Passion here shown forth
  Is the great pledge of sin forgiven ;
We praise Thee for Thy mercies sent
To us in this great Sacrament.

O HOLY SPIRIT, Who dost deign
  These earthly elements to bless,
Making the bread His Flesh to be,
  The wine His Blood, as we confess ;
We praise Thee for Thy mercies sent
To us in this great Sacrament.

Ye holy Angels, who, with us,
  Around GOD'S Altar lowly bow,
Adoring there the Crucified,
  Whose precious Death is pleaded now,
O praise Him for His mercies sent
To us in this great Sacrament.

Ye blessèd Saints, enthroned on high,
  Who once the paths of earth did tread,
Who reached in safety GOD'S abode,
  As strengthened by this Living Bread ;
O praise Him for His mercies sent
To us in this great Sacrament.

O Holy FATHER, Holy SON,
  And Holy SPIRIT, Whom we love,
Guide, strengthen, save us here below,
  And bring us to our home above,
To praise Thee for Thy mercies sent
To us in this great Sacrament.

G. BODY, 1874.

26

DUKE STREET.　　　　　　　　　L.M.　　　　　　　J. HATTON, 1793.

FIGHT the good fight with all thy might,
CHRIST is thy Strength, and CHRIST thy Right ;
Lay hold on life, and it shall be
Thy joy and crown eternally.

Run the straight race through GOD's good grace,
Lift up thine eyes, and seek His Face ;
Life with its way before us lies,
CHRIST is the path, and CHRIST the prize.

Cast care aside, lean on thy Guide,
His boundless mercy will provide ;
Trust, and thy trusting soul shall prove
CHRIST is its life, and CHRIST its love.

Faint not nor fear, His Arms are near,
He changeth not, and thou art dear ;
Only believe, and thou shalt see
That CHRIST is all in all to thee.

　　　　　　　　　J. S. B. MONSELL, 1863.

STAFFORD. 8.7.8.7. JOHANN GEORG CHRISTIAN STORL,
1676-1743.
Harmonised by S. S. WESLEY.

(Or 3, First Tune.)

FIRMLY I believe and truly
  GOD is Three, and GOD is One;
And I next acknowledge duly
  Manhood taken by the SON.

And I trust and hope most fully
  In that Manhood crucified;
And each thought and deed unruly
  Do to death, as He has died.

Simply to His grace and wholly
  Light and life and strength belong,
And I love supremely, solely,
  Him the Holy, Him the Strong.

And I hold in veneration
  For the love of Him alone,
Holy Church as His creation,
  And her teachings as His own.

Adoration aye be given
  With and through the Angelic host,
To the GOD of earth and heaven,
  FATHER, SON and HOLY GHOST.

J. H. NEWMAN, 1865.

28

EBENEZER.　　　　　　　　　8.7.8.7.D.　　　　　　　T. J. WILLIAMS.

REFRAIN.

(By permission of W. Gwenlyn Evans & Son, Carnarvon.)

From the depths of sin and failure,
　From despair as black as night,
Lord, we hear our brothers calling
　For deliv'rance and for light.

By the love that bore in silence
　Man's contempt and Satan's dart;
By the longing for the lost ones
　That consumes the Saviour's Heart.

Use us, Lord, to speed Thy kingdom ;
　Through us may Thy will be done ;
Give us eyes to see the vision
　Of a world redeem'd and won.

By the Saviour's Blood that bought us,
　By the peace His merits bring,
By the Spirit that constrains us
　Now on earth to crown Him King.

T. Rees, 1916.

29

GLORIOUS things of thee are spoken,
  Zion, city of our GOD ;
He Whose word cannot be broken
  Form'd thee for His own abode.
On the Rock of ages founded,
  What can shake thy sure repose ?
With salvation's walls surrounded,
  Thou may'st smile at all thy foes.

See, the streams of living waters,
  Springing from eternal love,
Well supply thy sons and daughters,
  And all fear of want remove.
Who can faint while such a river
  Ever flows their thirst to assuage—
Grace, which like the LORD the Giver,
  Never fails from age to age ?

Round each habitation hov'ring,
  See the cloud and fire appear,
For a glory and a cov'ring,
  Showing that the LORD is near.
Thus they march, the pillar leading,
  Light by night and shade by day ;
Daily on the manna feeding
  Which He gives them when they pray.

SAVIOUR, since of Zion's city
  I, through grace, a member am,
Let the world deride or pity,
  I will glory in Thy Name.
Fading is the world's best pleasure,
  All its boasted pomp and show ;
Solid joys and lasting treasure
  None but Zion's children know.

J. NEWTON, 1779.

30

REFRAIN.
Harmony.

Lift ye then your voi - ces; Swell the migh-ty flood

Loud-er still and loud - er Praise the Precious Blood.

GLORY be to JESUS,
  Who, in bitter pains,
Pour'd for me the Life-blood
  From His sacred Veins.

Grace and life eternal
  In that Blood I find ;
Blest be His compassion
  Infinitely kind.

Lift ye then your voices ;
  Swell the mighty flood ;
Louder still and louder
  Praise the precious Blood.

Blest through endless ages
Be the precious stream
Which from endless torments
Did the world redeem.

Abel's blood for vengeance
Pleaded to the skies;
But the Blood of JESUS
For our pardon cries.

Oft as it is sprinkled
On our guilty hearts,
Satan in confusion
Terror-struck departs;

Oft as earth exulting
Wafts its praise on high,
Angel-hosts rejoicing
Make their glad reply.

E. CASWALL, 1857.

*If the tune " Caswall " is used, the Refrain is sung only
after the last verse.*

30

CASWALL.
(*Second Tune.*)
6.5.6.5.
F. FILITZ, 1847.

(*or Tune* 68)

EVENTIDE.   10.10.10.10.   W. H. MONK, 1823-1889.

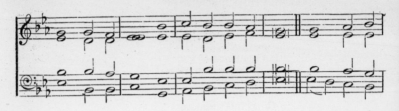

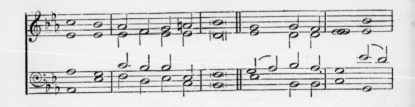

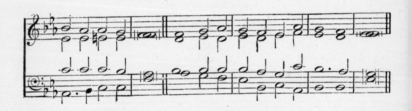

GOD made me for Himself, to serve Him here
With love's pure service and in filial fear;
To show His praise, for Him to labour now;
Then see His glory where the Angels bow.

All needful grace was mine, through His dear SON,
Whose life and death my full salvation won;
The grace that would have strengthen'd me, and
    taught;
Grace that would crown me when my work was
    wrought.

And I, poor sinner, cast it all away;
Lived for the toil or pleasure of each day;
As if no CHRIST had shed His precious Blood,
As if I owed no homage to my GOD.

O HOLY SPIRIT, with Thy fire Divine,
Melt into tears this thankless heart of mine;
Teach me to love what once I seem'd to hate,
And live to GOD, before it be too late.

H. W. BAKER, 1876.

32

GOD of Love, and Truth, and Beauty,
　Hallowed be Thy Name.
Fount of order, law and duty,
　Hallowed be Thy Name.
As in Heaven Thy hosts adore Thee,
And their faces veil before Thee,
So on earth, LORD, we implore Thee,
　Hallowed be Thy Name.

LORD, remove our guilty blindness,
　Hallowed be Thy Name.
Show Thy Heart of loving kindness,
　Hallowed be Thy Name.
By our heart's deep-felt contrition,
By our mind's enlightened vision,
By our will's complete submission,
　Hallowed be Thy Name.

In our worship, LORD, most holy,
　Hallowed be Thy Name.
In our work, however lowly,
　Hallowed be Thy Name.
In each heart's imagination,
In the Church's adoration,
In the conscience of the nation,
　Hallowed be Thy Name.

T. REES, 1916.

41

33

8.7.8.7.8.8.7.   *Geistliche Lieder (Wittenberg),*
1535.

GREAT GOD, what do I see and hear?
　The end of things created:
The Judge of all men doth appear
　On clouds of glory seated:
The trumpet sounds, the graves restore
The dead which they contain'd before;
　Prepare, my soul, to meet Him.

The dead in CHRIST shall first arise
　At that last trumpet's sounding;
Caught up to meet Him in the skies,
　With joy their LORD surrounding:
No gloomy fears their souls dismay;
His Presence sheds eternal day
　On those prepared to meet Him.

Th' ungodly, filled with guilty fears,
　Behold His wrath prevailing;
In woe they rise, but all their tears
　And sighs are unavailing:
The day of grace is past and gone;
Trembling they stand before His throne,
　All unprepared to meet Him.

Great Judge, to Thee our prayers we pour,
　In deep abasement bending;
O shield us through that last dread hour,
　Thy wondrous love extending:
May we, in this our trial day,
With faithful hearts Thy word obey,
　And thus prepare to meet Thee.

B. RINGWALDT, 1802, and others.

43

34

7.4.7.4.D.

Welsh Hymn Melody.

Voices in Unison

Org.

HAIL the day that sees Him rise,
To His Throne above the skies;
CHRIST, the LAMB for sinners given,
Enters now the highest Heav'n.

Alleluia !
Alleluia !
Alleluia !
Alleluia !

There for Him high triumph waits;
Lift your heads, eternal gates;
He hath conquered death and sin :
Take the King of Glory in.

Alleluia !
Alleluia !
Alleluia !
Alleluia !

Lo ! the Heav'n its LORD receives,
Yet He loves the earth He leaves ;
Though returning to His Throne,
Still He calls mankind His own.

Alleluia !
Alleluia !
Alleluia !
Alleluia !

See ! He lifts His Hands above ;
See ! He shows the prints of love ;
Hark ! His gracious Lips bestow
Blessings on His Church below.

Alleluia !
Alleluia !
Alleluia !
Alleluia !

Still for us He intercedes,
His prevailing Death He pleads,
Near Himself prepares our place,
He the first-fruits of our race.

Alleluia !
Alleluia !
Alleluia !
Alleluia !

LORD, though parted from our sight,
Far above the starry height,
Grant our hearts may thither rise,
Seeking Thee above the skies.

Alleluia !
Alleluia !
Alleluia !
Alleluia !

C. WESLEY, 1739.

35

No. LXI.   La Meuniere.   IRREGULAR.   *Nouveaux Cantiques Spirituels*
                                                   Provenceaux (Avignon), 1749.
                                                   Arr. by Bishop W. H. Frere, C.R.

Hark! a sweet voice calleth : "Come, follow Me,
Heed not what befalleth, but follow Me."

> *My soul rejoice,*
> *It is the Voice*
>   *Of Christ thy Saviour:*
> *Hearken to His call ;*
> *Follow, leaving all.*

" Leave all sinful pleasures, come, follow Me,
I have nobler treasures, so follow Me."

" I will all forgive thee, come, follow Me,
I will succour give thee, so follow Me."

" Take thy cross and bear it, come, follow Me,
I will with thee share it, so follow Me."

" Through the darkness wending, come, follow Me,
On to light unending, O follow Me."

" Death shall not us sever, come, follow Me,
Trust My love for ever, and follow Me."

T. Rees, C.R., 1916.

ST. BEES.　　　　　　　　7.7.7.7.　　　　　　J. B. DYKES, 1862.

HARK, my soul ! it is the LORD ;
'Tis thy SAVIOUR, hear His word ;
JESUS speaks, and speaks to thee,
" Say, poor sinner, lov'st thou Me ?

" I deliver'd thee when bound,
And, when bleeding, heal'd thy wound ;
Sought thee wandering, set thee right,
Turn'd thy darkness into light.

" Can a woman's tender care
Cease towards the child she bare ?
Yes, she may forgetful be,
Yet will I remember Thee.

" Mine is an unchanging love,
Higher than the heights above,
Deeper than the depths beneath,
Free and faithful, strong as death.

" Thou shalt see My glory soon,
When the work of grace is done ;
Partner of My Throne shalt be ;
Say, poor sinner, lov'st thou Me ? "

LORD, it is my chief complaint
That my love is weak and faint ;
Yet I love Thee and adore ;
O for grace to love Thee more.

W. COWPER, 1768.

37

PLEADING SAVIOUR.
In moderate time.

8.7.8.7.D.

*Plymouth Collection
(U.S.A.), 1855.*
Fine.

D.C

HE is pleading, by His sorrows,
　By the bitter pain He bore,
For the comfort of your pity—
　That your heart should love Him more.
Can you think of Him heart-broken,
　With His gentle Face so marred,
And pass on as tho' 'twere nothing
　That the outstretched Hands are scarred?

He is pleading, by your burdens,
　By your weariness and smart,
By life's wild unanswered questions,
　And your emptiness of heart.
Will you keep your care, unheeding
　The calm voice that offers rest?
And your soul drift, farther, farther,
　From the shelter of that Breast?

He is pleading, by the darkness
　Of the life without His light,
By the ever-thickening shadows,
　And the coming on of night;
Will you choose the deepening twilight
　With its final chill and gloom,
While sweet dawn breaks thro' the windows
　Of the brightening upper-room?

He is pleading, ever pleading,
　Here below, as there above,
By the FATHER'S perfect pity,
　And the SPIRIT'S tender love.
He is pleading, *now* is pleading
　With the sheep that He hath found—
Yield your heart, your life, to JESUS,
　That His love may fold you round.

W. ST. HILL BOURNE, 1846.

38

11.11.12.11.   *English Traditional Melody.*

(*From the English Hymnal, by permission of the Oxford University Press.*)

[Or A. & M. 676 (Supplement).]

He who would valiant be
'Gainst all disaster,
Let him in constancy
   Follow the Master.
There's no discouragement
Shall make him once relent
His first avowed intent
   To be a pilgrim.

Who so beset him round
With dismal stories,
Do but themselves confound:
   His strength the more is.
No foes shall stay his might,
Though he with giants fight:
He will make good his right
   To be a pilgrim.

Since, Lord, Thou dost defend
Us with Thy Spirit,
We know we at the end
   Shall life inherit.
Then fancies flee away!
I'll fear not what men say,
I'll labour night and day
   To be a pilgrim.

J. Bunyan, 1628-1688, and others.

39

ELLERS. 10.10.10.10. E. J. HOPKINS, 1869.

(By permission of Lady Carbery.)

HERE, O my LORD, I see Thee face to face ;
　Here faith can touch and handle things unseen ;
Here would I grasp with firmer hand Thy Grace,
　And all my weariness upon Thee lean.

Here would I feed upon the Bread of GOD ;
　Here drink with Thee the royal Wine of heaven ;
Here would I lay aside each earthly load,
　Here taste afresh the calm of sin forgiven.

I have no help but Thine ; nor do I need
　Another arm save Thine to lean upon ;
It is enough, my LORD—enough indeed ;
　My strength is in Thy might, Thy might alone.

Mine is the sin, but Thine the righteousness ;
　Mine is the guilt, but Thine the cleansing Blood ;
Here is my robe, my refuge, and my peace—
　Thy Blood, Thy righteousness, O LORD, my GOD.

H. BONAR, 1855.

40

IRREGULAR.

P. BLISS, 1871.

REFRAIN.

(By permission of Morgan & Scott Ltd.)

Ho, my comrades ! see the signal
  Waving in the sky !
Reinforcements now appearing,
  Victory is nigh !

" Hold the fort, for I am coming,"
  JESUS signals still ;
Wave the answer back to Heaven,
  " By Thy Grace we will."

See the mighty host advancing,
  Satan leading on :
Mighty men around us falling,
  Courage almost gone !

See the glorious banner waving !
  Hear the trumpet blow !
In our Leader's Name we'll triumph
  Over every foe.

Fierce and long the battle rages,
  But our help is near :
Onward comes our great Commander,
  Cheer, my comrades, cheer !

P. BLISS, 1871.

41

NICAEA.　　　　　　　11.12.12.10.　　　J. B. DYKES, 1823-1876.

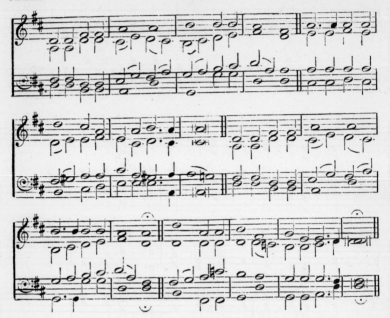

HOLY, Holy, Holy! LORD GOD Almighty!
　Early in the morning our song shall rise to Thee:
Holy, Holy, Holy! Merciful and Mighty!
　GOD in THREE Persons, Blessèd TRINITY!

Holy, Holy, Holy! all the Saints adore Thee,
　Casting down their golden crowns around the
　　glassy sea;
Cherubim and Seraphim falling down before Thee,
　Which wert, and art, and evermore shalt be.

Holy, Holy, Holy! though the darkness hide Thee,
　Though the eye of sinful man Thy glory may not
　　see,
Only Thou art Holy, there is none beside Thee,
　Perfect in power, in love, and purity.

Holy, Holy, Holy! LORD GOD Almighty!
　All Thy works shall praise Thy Name in earth, and
　　sky, and sea:
Holy, Holy, Holy! Merciful and Mighty!
　GOD in THREE PERSONS, Blessèd TRINITY.

　　　　　　　　　　　R. HEBER, 1827.

42

DEERHURST.   8.7.8.7.D.   J. LANGRAN, 1863.

(By permission of Novello & Co. Ltd.)   (Or Tune 103.)

HOLY SPIRIT, ever dwelling
  In the holiest realms of light :
Holy Spirit, ever brooding
  O'er a world of gloom and night :
Holy Spirit, ever raising
  Sons of earth to thrones on high :
Living, life-imparting Spirit,—
  Thee we praise and magnify.

Holy Spirit, ever breathing
  On the Church the breath of life :
Holy Spirit, through her waging
  With the world a ceaseless strife ;
Holy Spirit in her binding
  Age to age and soul to soul
In a fellowship unending,—
  Thee we worship and extol.

Holy Spirit, ever working
  Through the Church's ministry—
Quickening, strengthening, and absolving,
  Setting captive sinners free :
Holy Spirit, consecrating
  Every Eucharist on earth,—
Unto Thee be endless praises
  For Thy gifts of endless worth.

Holy Spirit, fount and channel
  Of the sevenfold gifts of grace,
May we in our hearts for ever
  Give to holy fear a place.
Fill our lives, O Lord, with worship,
  As with service gladly done ;
Bend our souls in adoration
  Of the eternal Three in One.

                                T. REES, 1922.

43

BROMSGROVE.   C.M.   COLLINS, 1789.

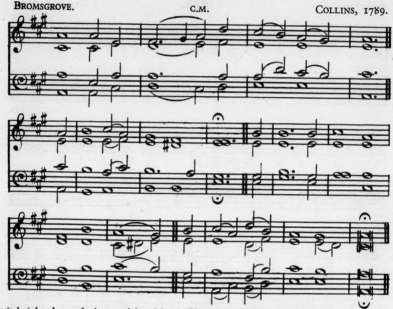

How bright these glorious spirits shine !
   Whence all their white array ?
How came they to the blissful seats
   Of everlasting day ?

Lo ! these are they from sufferings great
   Who came to realms of light,
And in the Blood of CHRIST have washed
   Those robes that shine so bright.

Now with triumphal palms they stand
   Before the Throne on high,
And serve the GOD they love amidst
   The glories of the sky.

Hunger and thirst are felt no more,
   Nor suns with scorching ray ;
GOD is their sun, Whose cheering beams
   Diffuse eternal day.

The LAMB Which dwells amidst the Throne,
   Shall o'er them still preside,
Feed them with nourishment Divine,
   And all their footsteps guide.

'Midst pastures green He'll lead His flock,
   Where living streams appear ;
And GOD the LORD from every eye
   Shall wipe off every tear.

To FATHER, SON, and HOLY GHOST,
   The GOD Whom we adore,
Be glory, as it was, is now,
   And shall be evermore.

I. WATTS and W. CAMERON, 1707.

44

ST. PETER.
(*First Tune.*)   C.M.   A. R. REINAGLE, 1799-1877.

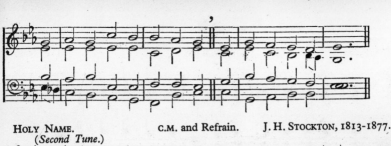

HOLY NAME.
(Second Tune.) C.M. and Refrain. J. H. STOCKTON, 1813-1877.

REFRAIN.

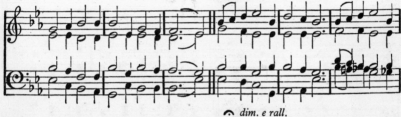

dim. e rall.

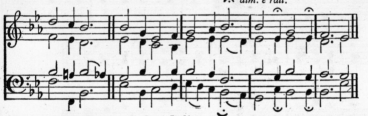

(By permission of Morgan & Scott Ltd.)

How sweet the Name of JESUS sounds
　In a believer's ear !
It soothes his sorrows, heals his wounds,
　And drives away his fear.

　Sweetest note in Seraph's song,
　Sweetest Name on mortal tongue,
　Sweetest carol ever sung,
　JESUS !—JESUS !—JESUS !

It makes the wounded spirit whole,
　And calms the troubled breast ;
'Tis manna to the hungry soul,
　And to the weary, rest.

Dear Name ! the rock on which I build,
　My shield and hiding-place,
My never-failing treasury, filled
　With boundless stores of grace.

JESUS ! my Shepherd, Husband, Friend,
　My Prophet, Priest, and King,
My Lord, my Life, my Way, my End,
　Accept the praise I bring.

Weak is the effort of my heart,
　And cold my warmest thought,
But when I see Thee as Thou art,
　I'll praise Thee as I ought.

　　Till then I would Thy love proclaim
　　　With every fleeting breath,
　　And may the music of Thy Name
　　　Refresh my soul in death.
　　　　　　　　J. NEWTON, 1779.
If the tune " St. Peter " is used, the refrain is not sung.

55

45

HUSH, my soul, what Voice is pleading?
 Thou canst feel its silent power :
Who is this that speaks so gently
 In this solemn evening hour?

"Stay, poor sinner, life is fleeting,
 And thy soul is dark within ;
Wilt thou wait till outer darkness
 Close in gloom thy life of sin?"

Hark! it is a Voice of sweetness,
 Tenderly it speaks, and true :
Dark and sad, yet strangely yearning
 For a peace I never knew.

Half inclined I stay and listen,
 Half inclined to go away,
Still I linger, for it whispers
 "Harden not thy heart to-day!"

What is this that steals upon me?
 Can it be that at my side,
In His own mysterious Presence,
 Stands the wondrous Crucified?

"Why, poor sinner, wilt thou linger?
 I am waiting to forgive ;
See the meaning of these wound-prints :
 I have died, that thou may'st live!"

Hush, my soul! it is thy SAVIOUR ;
 And He seeks His lost one now!
He is waiting ; flee not from Him,
 Venture near, before Him bow.

Tell thy sins ; He will forgive thee,
 And He will not love thee less ;
For the Human Heart of JESUS
 Overflows with tenderness.

J. H. LESTER, 1883.

46

CONVENTION.   IRREGULAR.   W. H. DOANE, 1832-1916.

REFRAIN.

(By permission of Morgan & Scott Ltd.)

AM Thine, O LORD; I have heard Thy Voice,
And it told Thy love to me;
ut I long to rise in the arms of faith,
And be closer drawn to Thee.

Draw me nearer, nearer, nearer, blessed
    LORD,
    To the Cross where Thou hast died.
Draw me nearer, nearer, nearer, blessed
    LORD,
    To Thy precious, bleeding side.

Consecrate me now to Thy service, LORD,
    By the power of Grace Divine.
Let my soul look up with a steadfast hope,
    And my will be lost in Thine.

Oh! the pure delight of a single hour,
    That before Thy Throne I spend,
When I kneel in prayer, and with Thee my
        GOD
    I commune as friend with friend.

There are depths of love that I cannot touch
    Till I cross the narrow sea;
There are heights of joy that I may not reach
    Till I rest in peace with Thee.
                    F. J. VAN ALSTYNE, 1875.

47

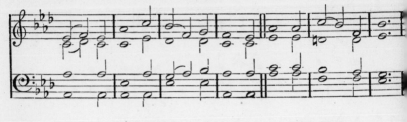

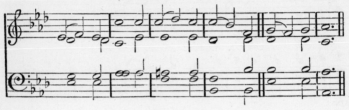

I AM trusting Thee, LORD JESUS,
   Trusting only Thee ;
Trusting Thee for full salvation,
   Great and free.

I am trusting Thee for pardon,
   At Thy feet I bow ;
For Thy grace and tender mercy
   Trusting now.

I am trusting Thee for cleansing,
   In the crimson flood ;
Trusting Thee to make me holy,
   By Thy Blood.

I am trusting Thee to guide me ;
   Thou alone shalt lead,
Every day and hour supplying
   All my need.

I am trusting Thee for power ;
   Thine can never fail :
Words which Thou Thyself shalt give me
   Must prevail.

I am trusting Thee, LORD JESUS,
   Never let me fall ;
I am trusting Thee for ever,
   And for all.

                   F. R. HAVERGAL, 1878.

48

(By permission of Morgan & Scott Ltd.)

I hear Thy welcome Voice,
  That calls me, Lord, to Thee,
For cleansing in the precious Blood
  That flow'd on Calvary.

    I am coming, Lord,
      Coming now to Thee,
    Wash me, cleanse me in the Blood
      That flow'd on Calvary.

Though coming weak and vile,
  Thou dost my strength assure :
Thou dost my vileness fully
    cleanse,
  Till spotless all and pure.

'Tis Jesus calls me on
  To perfect faith and love,
To perfect hope and peace and trust.
  For earth and Heaven above.

And He the witness gives
  To loyal hearts and free,
That every promise is fulfilled,
  If faith but bring the plea.

All hail, atoning Blood !
  All hail, redeeming Grace !
All hail, the gift of Christ our
    Lord,
  Our Strength and Righteousness.

            L. Hartsough, 1878.

49

KINGSFOLD.

D.C.M.

English Traditional Melody.
(Noted by L. E. BROADWOOD.)

Org.

(From the English Hymnal, by permission of the Oxford University Press.)

I HEARD the voice of JESUS say,
" Come unto Me and rest ;
Lay down, thou weary one, lay down
  Thy head upon My Breast " :
I came to JESUS as I was,
  Weary, and worn, and sad ;
I found in Him a resting-place,
  And He has made me glad.

I heard the voice of JESUS say,
" Behold, I freely give
The living water, thirsty one,
  Stoop down, and drink, and live : "
I came to JESUS, and I drank
  Of that life-giving stream ;
My thirst was quench'd, my soul revived,
  And now I live in Him.

I heard the voice of JESUS say,
" I am this dark world's Light,
Look unto Me, thy morn shall rise,
  And all thy day be bright : "
I look'd to JESUS, and I found
  In Him my Star, my Sun ;
And in that Light of life I'll walk
  Till travelling days are done.

H. BONAR, 1846.

* In verses 2 and 3 lines 5 and 6 run thus :

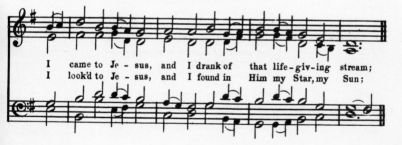

I came to Je - sus, and I drank of that life-giv-ing stream ;
I look'd to Je - sus, and I found in Him my Star, my Sun ;

50

6.6.6.6.

B. LUARD SELBY.

I HUNGER and I thirst ;
  JESU, my manna be ;
Ye living waters, burst
  Out of the rock for me.

Thou bruised and broken Bread,
  My lifelong wants supply ;
As living souls are fed,
  O feed me, or I die.

Thou true life-giving Vine,
  Let me Thy sweetness prove ;
Renew my life with Thine,
  Refresh my soul with love.

Rough paths my feet have trod,
  Since first their course began ;
Feed me, Thou Bread of GOD ;
  Help me, Thou SON of MAN.

For still the desert lies
  My thirsting soul before ;
O living waters, rise
  Within me evermore.

J. S. B. MONSELL, 1866.

51

I LOVE TO HEAR THE STORY.   7.6.7.6.D. and Refrain.   H. J. GAUNTLETT,
    In Unison.   1805-1876.

Fine.

D.C.

(Or 15, Second Tune.)

I LOVE to hear the story
    Which Angel voices tell,
How once the King of glory
    Came down on earth to dwell.
I am both weak and sinful,
    But this I surely know,
The LORD came down to save me,
    Because He loved me so.

I love to hear the story,
    Which Angel voices tell,
How once the King of glory
    Came down on earth to dwell.

I'm glad my blessèd SAVIOUR
    Was once a child like me,
To show how pure and holy
    His little ones might be ;
And if I try to follow
    His footsteps here below,
He never will forget me,
    Because He loves me so.

To sing His love and mercy
    My sweetest songs I'll raise ;
And though I cannot see Him,
    I know He hears my praise ;
For He has kindly promised
    That even I may go
To sing among His Angels,
    Because He loves me so.

E. M. MILLER, 1867.

52

I MET the Good Shepherd but now on the plain,
As homeward He carried His lost one again ;
I marvelled how gently His burden He bore,
And, as He passed by me, I knelt to adore.

O Shepherd, Good Shepherd, Thy Wounds they **are**
    deep,
The wolves have sore hurt Thee in saving Thy sheep ;
Thy raiment all over with crimson is dyed,
And what is this rent they have made in Thy Side ?

Ah, me ! how the thorns have entangled Thy Hair,
And cruelly riven that Forehead so fair !
How feebly Thou drawest Thy faltering Breath !
And lo, on Thy Face is the shadow of death !

O Shepherd, Good Shepherd ! and is it for me
This grievous affliction has fallen on Thee ?
Ah, then let me strive, for the love Thou hast borne,
To give Thee no longer occasion to mourn !

          E. Caswall, 1814-1876.

53

DEPENDENCE.   IRREGULAR.   R. Lowry, 1872.

REFRAIN.

(By permission of Morgan & Scott Ltd.)

I NEED Thee ev'ry hour, most gracious LORD,
No tender voice like Thine, can peace afford.

I need Thee, O I need Thee; ev'ry hour I need Thee;
O bless me now, my SAVIOUR! I come to Thee.

I need Thee ev'ry hour, stay Thou near by:
Temptations lose their power when Thou art nigh.

I need Thee ev'ry hour, in joy or pain:
Come quickly and abide, or life is vain.

I need Thee ev'ry hour, teach me Thy will;
And Thy rich promises in me fulfil.

A. S. HAWKES, 1872

54

Far Land.　　　IRREGULAR.　　　Ira D. Sankey, 1840-1908.

sostenuto.

Refrain.

(By permission of Morgan & Scott Ltd.)

In the land of strangers,
Whither thou art gone,
Hear a far Voice calling,
　My son! My son!

Welcome! wand'rer, welcome!
Welcome back to home.
Thou hast wander'd far away,
Come home! come home!

From the land of hunger,
Fainting, famished, lone,
Come to love and gladness,
　My son! My son!

See the door still open,
Thou art still My own;
Eyes of love are on thee,
　My son! My son!

See the well-spread table,
Unforgotten one!
Here are rest and plenty,
　My son! My son!

Thou art friendless, homeless,
Hopeless, and undone;
Mine is love unchanging,
　My son! My son!

H. Bonar, 1808-1889.

55

HERONGATE.   L.M.   *English Traditional Melody.*

(From the English Hymnal, by permission of the Oxford University Press.)

IT is a thing most wonderful,
   Almost too wonderful to be,
That GOD'S own SON should come from Heaven,
   And die to save a child like me.

And yet I know that it is true :
   He chose a poor and humble lot,
And wept, and toiled, and mourned, and died.
   For love of those who loved Him not.

I cannot tell how He could love
   A child so weak and full of sin ;
His love must be most wonderful,
   If He could die my love to win.

I sometimes think about the Cross,
   And shut my eyes, and try to see
The cruel nails and crown of thorns,
   And JESUS crucified for me.

But even could I see Him die,
   I could but see a little part
Of that great love, which, like a fire,
   Is always burning in His Heart.

It is most wonderful to know
   His love for me so free and sure ;
But 'tis more wonderful to see
   My love for Him so faint and poor.

And yet I want to love Thee, LORD ;
   O light the flame within my heart,
And I will love Thee more and more,
   Until I see Thee as Thou art.

                BP. W. WALSHAM HOW, 1872.

56

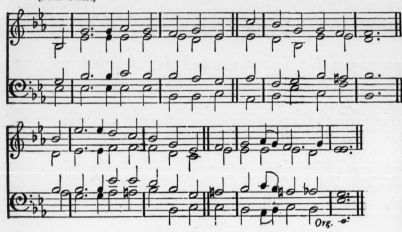

(By permission of Novello & Co. Ltd.)

I

JERUSALEM, my happy home,
  When shall I come to thee?
When shall my sorrows have an end?
  Thy joys when shall I see?

O happy harbour of the Saints,
  O sweet and pleasant soil!
In thee no sorrow may be found,
  No grief, no care, no toil.

No dampish mist is seen in thee,
  No cold nor darksome night;
There every soul shines as the sun;
  There GOD Himself gives light.

There lust and lucre cannot dwell,
  There envy bears no sway;
There is no hunger, heat nor cold,
  But pleasure every way.

Jerusalem! Jerusalem!
  GOD grant I once may see
Thy endless joys, and of the same
  Partaker aye may be.

Thy walls are made of precious stones,
  Thy bulwarks diamonds square,
Thy gates are of right orient pearl,
  Exceeding rich and rare.

Thy turrets and thy pinnacles
  With carbuncles do shine,
Thy very streets are paved with gold,
  Surpassing clear and fine.

Thy houses are of ivory,
  Thy windows crystal clear,
Thy tiles are made of beaten gold—
  O GOD, that I were there!

II

THY Saints are crowned with glory great,
  They see GOD face to face,
They triumph still, they still rejoice,
  Most happy is their case.

There David stands with harp in hand,
  As master of the choir,
Ten thousand times that man were blest,
  That might this music hear.

Our Lady sings Magnificat
  With tune surpassing sweet,
And all the virgins bear their part,
  Sitting about her feet.

Te Deum doth S. Ambrose sing,
  S. Austin doth the like;
Old Simeon and Zachary
  Have not their songs to seek.

There Magdalen hath left her moan,
  And cheerfully doth sing,
With blessèd Saints whose harmony
  In ev'ry street doth ring.

Jerusalem my happy home,
  When shall I come to thee?
When shall my labours have an end?
  Thy joys when shall I see?

F. B. P., 16th century.

FULSTOW.
(*First Tune.*)

6.5.6.5.

T. R. MATTHEWS.

(*By permission of Novello & Co. Ltd.*)

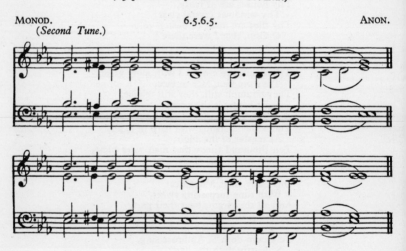

MONOD.
(*Second Tune.*)

6.5.6.5.

ANON.

JESU, gentlest SAVIOUR,
  GOD of might and power,
Thou Thyself art dwelling
  In us at this hour.

Nature cannot hold Thee,
  Heaven is all too strait
For Thine endless glory
  And Thy royal state.

Out beyond the shining
  Of the furthest star
Thou art ever stretching
  Infinitely far.

Yet the hearts of children
  Hold what worlds cannot,
And the GOD of wonders
  Loves the lowly spot.

JESU, gentlest SAVIOUR,
  Thou art in us now;
Fill us full of goodness
  Till our hearts o'erflow.

Multiply our graces,
  Chiefly love and fear,
And, dear LORD, the chiefest,
  Grace to persevere.

F. W. FABER, 1854.

58

7.7.7.7.D.

J. B. DYKES, 1861.

(Or Tune 120.)

JESU, Lover of my soul,
  Let me to Thy Bosom fly,
While the gathering waters roll,
  While the tempest still is high.
Hide me, O my SAVIOUR, hide,
  Till the storm of life be past;
Safe into the haven guide,
  O receive my soul at last.

Other refuge have I none;
  Hangs my helpless soul on Thee;
Leave, ah! leave me not alone,
  Still support and comfort me.
All my trust on Thee is stayed,
  All my help from Thee I bring;
Cover my defenceless head
  With the shadow of Thy wing.

Plenteous grace with Thee is found,
  Grace to cover all my sin;
Let the healing streams abound,
  Make and keep me pure within.
Thou of life the fountain art,
  Freely let me take of Thee:
Spring Thou up within my heart,
  Rise to all eternity.

C. WESLEY, 1740.

71

59

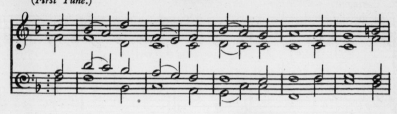

Refrain

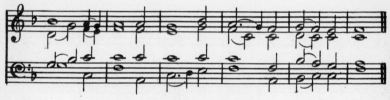

Jesu, my Lord, my God, my All,
Hear me, blest Saviour, when I call;
Hear me, and from Thy dwelling-place
Pour down the riches of Thy grace.

Jesu, my Lord, I Thee adore ;
O ! make me love Thee more and more.

Jesu, too late I Thee have sought,
How can I love Thee as I ought ?
And how extol Thy matchless fame,
The glorious beauty of Thy Name ?

Jesu, what didst Thou find in me,
That Thou hast dealt so lovingly ?
How great the joy that Thou hast brought,
So far exceeding hope or thought !

Jesu, of Thee shall be my song ;
To Thee my heart and soul belong.
All that I am or have is Thine ;
And Thou, my Saviour, Thou art mine.

H. COLLINS, 1854.

59

ST. CATHERINE.
(*Second Tune.*)

8.8.8.8.8.8.

H. F. HEMEY and
J. G. WALTON, 1907.

REFRAIN.

(Or Tune 25.)

60

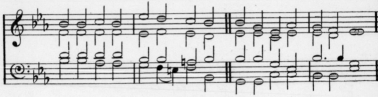

(By permission of the Proprietors of Hymns A. & M.)

Jesus ! Refuge of the weary !
    Object of the spirit's love ;
Fountain in life's desert dreary,
    Saviour from the world above.

O how oft Thine Eyes offended,
    Gaze upon the sinner's fall ;
Yet Thou, on the Cross extended,
    Bore the penalty for all.

Yet, no vow repentant breathing,
    Still we pass Thy sacred Cross,
Though, 'neath thorns Thy Forehead wreathing,
    Dropped the Bloody Sweat for us.

Yet Thy sinless Death hath bought us
    Life eternal, peace and rest ;
What Thy Grace alone hath taught us
    Calms the sinner's stormy breast.

Jesus ! would our hearts were burning
    With more fervent love for Thee,
Would our eyes were ever turning
    To Thy Cross of agony.

So, in pain and rapture blending,
    Might our failing eyes grow dim,
While the heart would soar ascending
    To the circling Cherubim.

Then in glory, parted never
    From the Blessèd Saviour's Side,
Graven on our hearts for ever
    Be the Cross and Crucified.

Then the Wounds with which He bought us
    We shall worship evermore ;
And the Shepherd Good, Who sought us,
    With enraptured hearts adore.

P. Doddridge, 1755.

61

MERTON.

8.7.8.7.

W. H. MONK, 1823-1889.

(Or Tune 183.)

JESUS calls us!—o'er the tumult
 Of our life's wild restless sea,
Day by day His sweet Voice soundeth,
 Saying, " Christian, follow Me ".

As of old Saint Andrew heard it
 By the Galilean lake,
Turned from home, and toil, and kindred,
 Leaving all for His dear sake.

JESUS calls us from the worship
 Of the vain world's golden store,
From each idol that would keep us,
 Saying, " Christian, love Me more."

In our joys and in our sorrows,
 Days of toil and hours of ease,
Still He calls, in cares and pleasures,
 That we love Him more than these.

JESUS calls us!—by Thy mercies,
 SAVIOUR, make us hear Thy call,
Give our hearts to Thine obedience,
 Serve and love Thee best of all.

C. F. ALEXANDER, 1852.

EASTER HYMN.

7.4.7.4.D.

Altered from melody in
"Lyra Davidica," 1708.

JESUS CHRIST is risen to-day,

Alleluia !

Our triumphant holy day,

Alleluia !

Who did once upon the Cross

Alleluia !

Suffer to redeem our loss.

Alleluia !

Hymns of praise then let us sing

Alleluia !

Unto CHRIST, our heavenly King,

Alleluia !

Who endured the cross and grave,

Alleluia !

Sinners to redeem and save.

Alleluia !

But the pain which He endured

Alleluia !

Our salvation hath procured ;

Alleluia !

Now above the sky He's King,

Alleluia !

Where the Angels ever sing.

Alleluia !   ANON., 1708.

63

St. Oswald.

8.7.8.7.

J. B. Dykes, 1857.

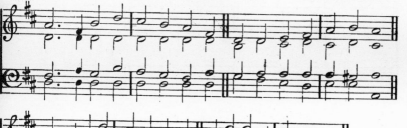

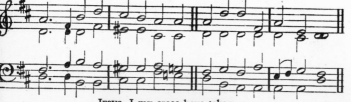

Jesus, I my cross have taken,
  All to leave and follow Thee;
Destitute, despised, forsaken,
  Thou from hence my all shalt be.

Perish every fond ambition,
  All I've sought, or hoped, or known;
Yet how rich is my condition,
  God and Heaven are still my own.

Let the world despise and leave me,
  They have left my Saviour too;
Human hearts and looks deceive me;
  Thou art not, like them, untrue.

And while Thou shalt smile upon me,
  God of wisdom, love and might,
Foes may hate, and friends may shun me;
  Show Thy face and all is bright.

Take, my soul, thy full salvation,
  Rise o'er sin, and fear, and care,
Joy to find in every station
  Something still to do or bear.

Think what spirit dwells within thee,
  What a Father's smile is thine,
What a Saviour died to win thee,
  Child of heaven, shouldst thou repine?

Haste, then, on from grace to glory,
  Arm'd by faith, and wing'd by prayer,
Heaven's eternal day's before thee,
  God's own Hand shall guide thee there.

Soon shall close thine earthly mission,
  Swift shall pass thy pilgrim days,
Hope soon change to glad fruition,
  Faith to sight, and prayer to praise.

H. F. Lyte, 1824.

64

6.5.6.5.D.

Bible Class Magazine, 1860.

JESUS, I will trust Thee, trust Thee with my soul ;
Guilty, lost, and helpless, Thou canst make me whole.
There is none in Heaven or on earth like Thee :
Thou hast died for sinners—therefore, LORD, for me.

JESUS, I may trust Thee, Name of matchless worth,
Spoken by the Angel at Thy wondrous Birth ;
Written, and for ever, on Thy Cross of shame,
Sinners read and worship, trusting in that Name.

JESUS, I must trust Thee, pondering Thy ways,
Full of love and mercy all Thine earthly days :
Sinners gathered round Thee, lepers sought Thy Face—
None too vile or loathsome for a SAVIOUR'S Grace.

JESUS, I can trust Thee, trust Thy written word,
Though Thy Voice of pity I have never heard ;
When Thy SPIRIT teacheth, to my taste how sweet—
Only may I hearken, sitting at Thy Feet.

JESUS, I do trust Thee, trust without a doubt,
Whosoever cometh, Thou wilt not cast out ;
Faithful is Thy promise, precious is Thy Blood,
These my soul's salvation, Thou my SAVIOUR, GOD !

M. J. WALKER, 1855.

65

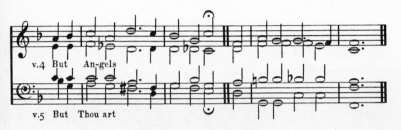

v.4 But An-gels

v.5 But Thou art

Jesus, in Thy dear Sacrament,
    Thy Cross I cannot see,
But the Crucified is offer'd there,
    And He was slain for me.

Jesus, in Thy dear Sacrament,
    Thy Flesh I cannot see,
But that Flesh is given to be our food,
    And It was scourged for me.

Jesus, in Thy dear Sacrament,
    Thy Blood I cannot see,
But the Chalice glows with those red drops,
    On Calv'ry shed for me.

Jesus, in Thy dear Sacrament,
    Thy Face I cannot see,
But Angels there behold the Brow
    Thorn-crown'd for love of me.

Jesus, my Maker and my God,
    Thy Godhead none may see,
But Thou art present, God and Man,
    In Thy Sacrament with me.

H. N. Oxenham.

66

NEAR THE CROSS.   IRREGULAR.   W. H. DOANE, 1832-1916.

REFRAIN.

(*By permission of Morgan & Scott Ltd.*)

Jesus, keep me near the Cross,
  There a precious fountain,
Free to all—a healing stream—
  Flows from Calv'ry's mountain.

In the Cross, in the Cross,
  Be my glory ever;
Till my raptured soul shall find
  Rest beyond the river.

Near the Cross, a trembling soul,
  Love and mercy found me ;
There a Bright and Morning Star
  Shed its beams around me.

Near the Cross ! O Lamb of God,
  Bring its scenes before me ,
Help me walk from day to day,
  With its shadow o'er me.

Near the Cross I'll watch and wait,
  Hoping, trusting, ever,
Till I reach the golden strand,
  Just beyond the river.

F. J. Van Alstyne, 1869.

67

St. Albinus.   7.8.7.8.4.   H. J. Gauntlett, 1852.

Al - le - lu - ia.

Jesus lives ! thy terrors now
  Can, O death, no more appal us ;
Jesus lives ! by this we know
  Thou, O grave, canst not enthral us.
                  Alleluia !

Jesus lives ! henceforth is death
  But the gate of life immortal ;
This shall calm our trembling breath,
  When we pass its gloomy portal.
                  Alleluia !

Jesus lives ! for us He died :
  Then, alone to Jesus living,
Pure in heart may we abide,
  Glory to our Saviour giving.
                  Alleluia !

Jesus lives ! our hearts know well
  Nought from us His love shall sever ;
Life, nor death, nor powers of hell
  Tear us from His keeping ever.
                  Alleluia !

Jesus lives ! to Him the throne
  Over all the world is given ;
May we go where He is gone,
  Rest and reign with Him in Heaven.
                  Alleluia !
              C. F. Gellert, 1757.

68

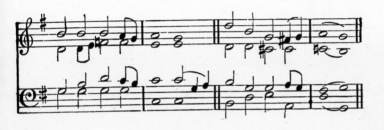

JESUS ! stand among us
In Thy risen power,
Let this time of worship
Be a hallowed hour.

Breathe Thy HOLY SPIRIT
Into every heart,
Bid the fears and sorrows
From each soul depart.

Thus with quickened footsteps
We pursue our way,
Watching for the dawning
Of th' Eternal Day !
　　　　　　W. PENNEFATHER, 1872.

69

(Or Tune 114.)

JESUS! speak to me in love,
　Restless, storm-tossed in my sin,
With Thy mighty Voice, O LORD,
　Thy great calm create within;
Bid the stormy winds to cease,
Bid, O bid me go in peace.

To Thee, JESU, do I fly,
　Wakened from my soul's dread sleep;
None but Thou canst save me, LORD,
　In this hour of anguish deep;
Thou alone canst give release,
Bid, O bid me go in peace.

Boldly at Thy Throne of Grace,
　LORD, I now forgiveness seek;
In Thy tender, pitying Love,
　To my soul Thy pardon speak.
JESU! make my anguish cease,
Bid, O bid me go in peace.

Prince of Peace! who in Thy death
　Didst for me the ransom pay,
Cleanse me in Thy precious Blood,
　Give to me Thy peace to-day.
Now, LORD, grant my soul release,
Now, LORD, bid me go in peace.

G. BODY, 1874.

70

8.7.8.7.8.7. *Welsh Traditional Melody.*

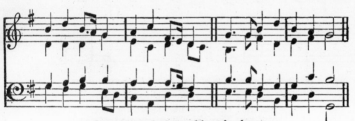

JUDGE eternal, throned in splendour,
  LORD of lords and King of kings,
With Thy living fire of judgement
  Purge this realm of bitter things :
Solace all its wide dominion
  With the healing of Thy wings.

Still the weary folk are pining
  For the hour that brings release :
And the city's crowded clangour
  Cries aloud for sin to cease ;
And the homesteads and the woodlands
  Plead in silence for their peace.

Crown, O GOD, Thine own endeavour,
  Cleave our darkness with Thy sword :
Feed the faint and hungry heathen
  With the richness of Thy Word :
Cleanse the body of this empire
  Through the glory of the LORD.

H. SCOTT HOLLAND, 1906.

85

71

SAFFRON WALDEN. 8.8.8.6. A. H. BROWN, 1830-1926.

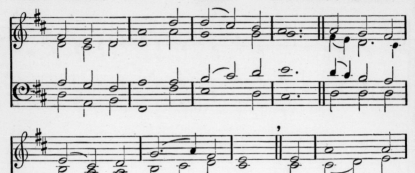

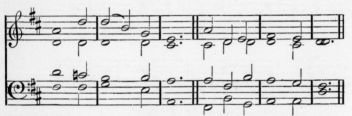

(From the English Hymnal, by permission of the Oxford University Press.)

JUST as I am, without one plea
But that Thy Blood was shed for me,
And that Thou bidd'st me come to Thee,
O LAMB of GOD, I come.

Just as I am, though toss'd about
With many a conflict, many a doubt,
Fightings and fears within, without,

Just as I am, poor, wretched, blind;
Sight, riches, healing of the mind,
Yea, all I need, in Thee to find,

Just as I am, Thou wilt receive,
Wilt welcome, pardon cleanse, relieve;
Because Thy promise I believe,

Just as I am (Thy love unknown
Has broken every barrier down),
Now to be Thine, yea, Thine alone,

Just as I am, of that free love
The breadth, length, depth, and height to prove,
Here for a season, then above,

C. ELLIOTT, 1836.

86

KNOCKING.   IRREGULAR.   G. F. ROOT, 1874.

(By permission of Morgan & Scott Ltd.)

KNOCKING, knocking! who is there?
Waiting, waiting, O how fair!
'Tis a Pilgrim, strange and kingly,
   Never such was seen before;
Ah! my soul, for such a wonder,
   Wilt thou not undo the door?

Knocking, knocking; still He's there!
Waiting, waiting, wondrous fair;
But the door is hard to open,
   For the weeds and ivy-vine,
With their dark and clinging tendrils,
   Ever round the hinges twine.

Knocking, knocking—what! still there?
Waiting, waiting, grand and fair;
Yes, the piercèd Hand still knocketh,
   And beneath the crownèd Hair
Beam the patient Eyes, so tender,
   Of thy SAVIOUR waiting there.

H. STOWE, 1867.

73

LEAD, kindly Light, amid the encircling gloom,
    Lead Thou me on ;
The night is dark, and I am far from home,
    Lead Thou me on.
Keep Thou my feet ; I do not ask to see
The distant scene ; one step enough for me.

I was not ever thus, nor prayed that Thou
        Shouldst lead me on ;
I loved to choose and see my path ; but now
        Lead Thou me on.
I loved the garish day, and, spite of fears,
Pride ruled my will : remember not past years.

So long Thy power hath blest me, sure it still
        Will lead me on
O'er moor and fen, o'er crag and torrent, till
        The night is gone,
And with the morn those Angel faces smile,
Which I have loved long since, and lost awhile.

J. H. NEWMAN, 1834.

73

SANDON.
(*Second Tune.*)

10.4.10.4.10.10.

C. H. PURDAY, 1860.

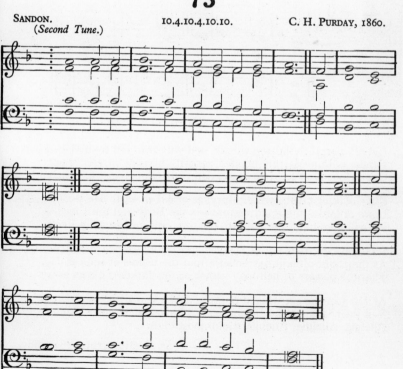

74

PICARDY.   8.7.8.7.8.7.   *French Traditional Carol.*

In Unison.

(From the English Hymnal.)

Let all mortal flesh keep silence, and with fear and trembling stand;
Ponder nothing earthly-minded, for with blessing in His Hand,
CHRIST our GOD to earth descendeth, our full homage to demand.

King of kings, yet born of Mary, as of old on earth He stood,
LORD of lords, in human vesture—in the Body and the Blood—
He will give to all the faithful His own Self for heavenly Food.

Rank on rank the host of Heaven spreads its vanguard on the way,
As the Light of light descendeth from the realms of endless day,
That the powers of hell may vanish as the darkness clears away.

At His feet the six-winged Seraph; Cherubim with sleepless eye,
Veil their faces to the Presence, as with ceaseless voice they cry,
Alleluia, Alleluia, Alleluia, LORD most high.

Tr. G. MOULTRIE, 1829-1885.

75

FATHER HENRY.
(First Tune.)

9.6.9.6.

J. G. ADDERLEY.

IGNATIUS.
(Second Tune.)

9.6.9.6.

J. H. LESTER.

LET me come closer to Thee, JESUS;
  O! closer day by day,
Let me lean harder on Thee, JESUS,
  Yes, harder all the way.

Let me show forth Thy beauty, JESUS,
  Like sunshine on the hills.
O! let my lips pour forth Thy sweetness
  In joyous sparkling rills.

Yes, like a fountain, precious JESUS,
  Make me and let me be;
Keep me and use me daily, JESUS,
  For Thee, for only Thee.

In all my heart and will, O JESUS,
  Be altogether King,
Make me a loyal subject, JESUS,
  To Thee in everything.

Thirsting and hungering for Thee, JESUS,
  With blessed hunger here;
Longing for home on Zion's mountain,—
  No thirst, no hunger there.

FR. IGNATIUS, O.S.B., 1883.

91

76

CRUCIFER.　　　　　　　10.10. and Refrain.　　　　S. H. NICHOLSON, 1916.

Lift high the Cross, the love of CHRIST pro - claim

Till all the world .... a - dore .... His sa - cred Name.

(*Copyright, 1915, by the Proprietors of Hymns A. & M.*)

LIFT high the Cross, the love of CHRIST proclaim
Till all the world adore His Sacred Name.

Come, brethren, follow where our Captain trod,
Our King victorious, CHRIST the SON of GOD.

Lift high the Cross, the love of CHRIST proclaim,
Till all the world adore His Sacred Name.

Led on their way by this triumphant sign,
The hosts of GOD in conquering ranks combine.

Each new-born soldier of the Crucified
Bears on his brow the seal of Him Who died.

This is the sign which Satan's legions fear,
The mystery which Angel hosts revere.

Saved by this Cross whereon their LORD was slain,
The sons of Adam their lost home regain.

From north and south, from east and west they raise
In growing unison their song of praise.

O LORD, once lifted on the glorious Tree,
As Thou hast promised, draw men unto Thee.

Let every race and every language tell
Of Him Who saves our souls from death and hell.

From farthest regions let them homage bring
And on His Cross adore their SAVIOUR KING.

Set up Thy Throne, that earth's despair may cease
Beneath the shadow of its healing peace.

So shall our song of triumph ever be,
Praise to the Crucified for victory.

G. W. KITCHIN and M. R. NEWBOLT, 1887.

77

8.7.8.7.4.7.   *English Melody of the*
                                                                    Eighteenth Century.

(May be sung in unison throughout.)

Lo ! He comes with clouds descending,
  Once for favoured sinners slain ;
Thousand thousand Saints attending,
  Swell the triumph of His train ;
    Alleluia !
God appears on earth to reign.

Every eye shall now behold Him,
  Robed in dreadful majesty ;
Those who set at nought and sold Him,
  Pierced and nailed Him to the Tree,
    Deeply wailing,
Shall the true MESSIAH see.

Every island, sea, and mountain,
  Heaven and earth, shall flee away ;
All who hate Him must, confounded,
  Hear the trump proclaim the day :
    Come to Judgment !
Come to Judgment, come away !

Blest redemption, long expected,
  See ! His solemn pomp to share,
All His Saints, by men rejected,
  Rise to meet Him in the air :
    Alleluia !
See the day of GOD appear !

Yea, Amen, let all adore Thee,
  High on Thine eternal Throne !
SAVIOUR, take the power and glory,
  Claim the kingdom for Thine own ;
    O come quickly !
Alleluia ! come, LORD, come !

J. CENNICK and C. WESLEY, 1758.

78

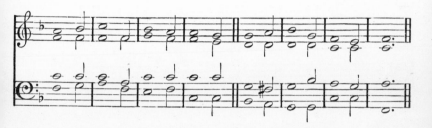

LORD, I hear of showers of blessings
  Thou art scattering full and free ;
Showers, the thirsty land refreshing :
  Let Thy grace descend on me.

    Even me ! even me !
    *   *Let Thy grace descend on me.*

Pass me not ! O gracious FATHER !
  Sinful though my heart may be ;
Thou might'st leave me, but the rather
  Let Thy mercy light on me.

Pass me not ! O tender SAVIOUR;
  Let me love and cling to Thee ;
I am longing for Thy favour !
  Whilst Thou'rt calling, O call me.

Pass me not ! O mighty SPIRIT !
  Thou canst make the blind to see ;
Witnesser of JESU's merit,
  Speak the word of power to me.

Have I long in sin been sleeping—
  Long been slighting, grieving Thee?
Has the world my heart been keeping ?
  O forgive and rescue me.

Love of GOD, so pure and changeless !
  Blood of CHRIST, so rich and free !
Grace of GOD, so strong and boundless !
  Magnify it all in me.

Pass me not—but, pardon bringing,
  Bind my heart, O LORD, to Thee ;
Whilst the streams of life are springing,
  Blessing others, O bless me.

                E. CODNOR, 1860.

    * *Repeat the fourth line of each verse.*

79

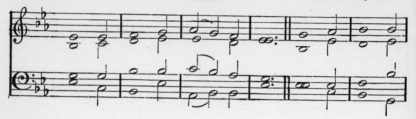

Lord, in this Thy mercy's day,
Ere it pass for aye away,
On our knees we fall and pray.

Holy Jesu, grant us tears,
Fill us with heart-searching fears,
Ere that awful doom appears.

Lord, on us Thy Spirit pour,
Kneeling lowly at the door,
Ere it close for evermore.

By Thy night of agony,
By Thy supplicating cry,
By Thy willingness to die.

By Thy tears of bitter woe
For Jerusalem below,
Let us not Thy love forgo.

Grant us 'neath Thy wings a place,
Lest we lose this day of grace,
Ere our eyes behold Thy Face.

I. Williams, 1844.

80

HOLLEY.

L.M.

G. HEWS, 1835.

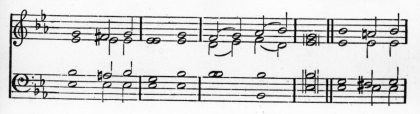

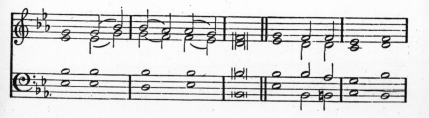

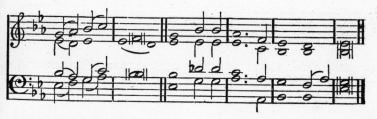

LORD, speak to me, that I may speak
 In living echoes of Thy tone ;
As Thou hast sought, so let me seek
 Thy erring children lost and lone.

Oh lead me, LORD, that I may lead
 The wandering and the wavering feet ;
Oh feed me, LORD, that I may feed
 The hungering ones with manna sweet.

Oh strengthen me that while I stand
 Firm on the Rock, and strong in Thee,
I may stretch out a loving hand
 To wrestlers with the troubled sea.

Oh teach me, LORD, that I may teach
 The precious things Thou dost impart ;
And wing my words, that they may reach
 The hidden depths of many a heart.

Oh give Thine own sweet rest to me,
 That I may speak with soothing power
A word in season, as from Thee,
 To weary ones in needful hour.

Oh fill me with Thy fullness, LORD,
 Until my very heart o'erflow
In kindling thought and glowing word,
 Thy love to tell, Thy praise to show.

Oh use me, LORD, use even me,
 Just as Thou wilt, and when, and where ;
Until Thy blessèd Face I see,
 Thy rest, Thy joy, Thy glory share.

F. R. HAVERGAL, 1872.

97

81

8.7.8.7.D.

S. S. WESLEY.

LORD, Thy ransomed Church is waking
    Out of slumber far and near,
Knowing that the morn is breaking
    When the Bridegroom shall appear;
Waking up to claim the treasure
    With Thy precious Life-blood bought,
And to trust in fuller measure
    All Thy wondrous Death hath wrought.

Praise to Thee for this glad shower,
    Precious drops of latter rain,
Praise, that by Thy SPIRIT's power
    Thou hast quickened us again—
That Thy Gospel's priceless treasure
    Now is borne from land to land,
And that all the FATHER's pleasure
    Prospers in Thy piercèd Hand.

Praise to Thee for saved ones yearning
    O'er the lost and wandering throng,
Praise for voices daily learning
    To upraise the glad new song:
Praise to Thee for sick ones hasting
    Now to touch Thy garment's hem;
Praise for souls believing, tasting
    All Thy love has won for them.

Set our hearts, O LORD, on fire
    With the love of Thy dear Name;
Touch our lips, our souls inspire
    Now to spread abroad Thy fame;
Fix our eyes on Thy returning,
    Keeping watch till Thou shalt come ;—
Loins well girt, lamps brightly burning;
    Then, LORD, take Thy servants home.

S. G. STOCK, 1874.

82

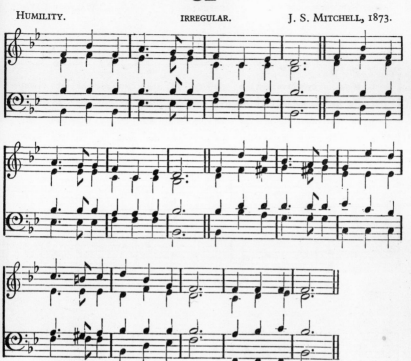

Low at Thy piercèd Feet,
  SAVIOUR of all,
Helpless and sorrowful,
  Prostrate I fall.
O cast me not away,
Forgive my sin this day—
  Forgive my sin,
  All, all my sin.

Sinful my life has been,
  Unclean, unclean;
All my iniquity
  Thine eye hath seen.
Cleanse Thou my soul to-day,
Wash all my sins away,
  In Thine own Blood,
  Thy precious Blood.

By all Thy grief and pain,
  Forgive me now;
Before Thy Cross in shame
  Lowly I bow.
LORD, let that Blood of Thine
Wash now this soul of mine—
  Wash Thou my soul,
  My guilty soul.

Thou didst for me endure
  Dread Calvary,
Sin's punishment and shame—
  All, all for me.
On Thee my guilt was laid,
By Thee my debt was paid,
  To set me free,
  And keep me free.

LORD, I accept Thee now,
  Accept Thou me;
I have delayed too long,
  And grievèd Thee.
By all Thy love to me
I give myself to Thee;
  Make me Thine own,
  All, all Thine own.

J. STEPHENS, 1863.

99

MINE EYES HAVE SEEN
THE GLORY.

IRREGULAR.

H. WALFORD DAVIES.

1. Mine   eyes have seen the   glo - ry   of the   com - ing of   the LORD;
2. He hath sound-ed forth the   trum - pet that shall nev - er call   re - treat·
3. In   the   beau - ty of the   lil - ies CHRIST was born   a - cross the   sea,
4. He   is   com - ing like the   glo - ry   of the   morn - ing on   the wave;

Fervently.

1. He   is   tram - pling out   the   vin - tage where the grapes of   wrath are   stored;
2. He   is   sift - ing out   the   hearts of   men be - fore His Judge-ment seat:
3. With a   glo - ry   in His   Bo - som that trans - fig - ures   you   and   me;
4. He   is   wis - dom to the   migh - ty: He is   suc - cour   to   the brave.

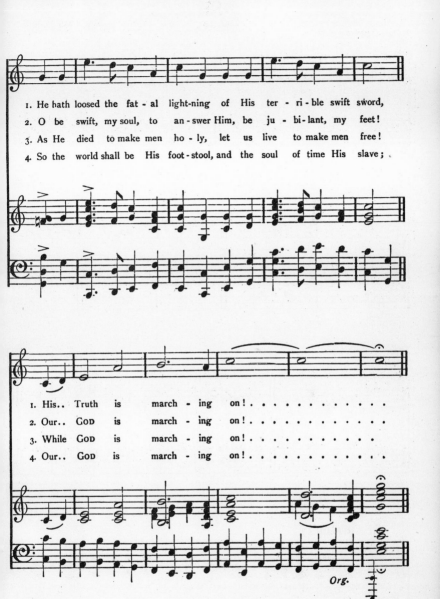

1. He hath loosed the fat - al light-ning of His ter - ri - ble swift sword,
2. O be swift, my soul, to an - swer Him, be ju - bi - lant, my feet!
3. As He died to make men ho - ly, let us live to make men free!
4. So the world shall be His foot - stool, and the soul of time His slave;

1. His.. Truth is march - ing on!. . . . .
2. Our.. GOD is march - ing on!. . . . .
3. While GOD is march - ing on!. . . . .
4. Our.. GOD is march - ing on!. . . . .

Org.

JULIA WARD HOWE, c. 1862.

84

IRCHESTER.

H. R. PALMER, 1834-1907.

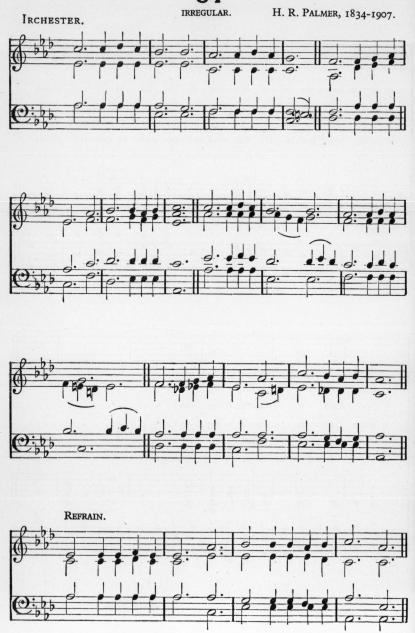

REFRAIN.

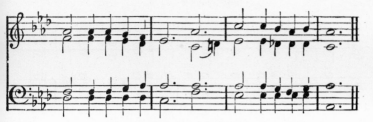

(By permission of Morgan & Scott Ltd.)

MORE holiness give me,
 More sweetness within ;
More patience in suff'ring,
 More sorrow for sin ;
More faith in my SAVIOUR,
 More sense of His care ;
More joy in His service,
 More purpose in prayer.

Come, my SAVIOUR, and help me,
 Comfort, strengthen, and keep me ;
Thou each moment wilt save me ;
 Thou art saving me now.

More gratitude give me,
 More trust in the LORD ;
More pride in His glory,
 More hope in His word ;
More tears for His sorrows,
 More pain at His grief ;
More meekness in trial,
 More praise for relief.

More purity give me,
 More strength to o'ercome ;
More freedom from earth-stains,
 More longing for home ;
More fit for the kingdom,
 More used would I be ;
More blessed and holy,
 More, SAVIOUR, like Thee.

P. BLISS, 1873.

85

OLIVET.   6.6.4.6.6.6.4.   L. MASON, 1833.

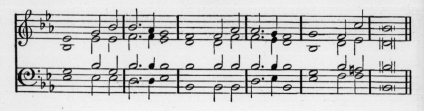

My faith looks up to Thee,
Thou LAMB of Calvary,
  SAVIOUR Divine !
Now hear me while I pray,
Take all my guilt away,
O let me from this day
  Be wholly Thine.

May Thy rich Grace impart
Strength to my fainting heart,
  My zeal inspire ;
As Thou hast died for me,
O may my love to Thee
Pure, warm and changeless be,
  A living fire.

While life's dark maze I tread,
And griefs around me spread,
  Be Thou my guide ;
Bid darkness turn to day,
Wipe sorrow's tears away,
Nor let me ever stray
  From Thee aside.

When ends life's transient dream,
When death's cold, sullen stream
  Shall o'er me roll,
Blest SAVIOUR, then in love
Fear and distrust remove ;
O bear me safe above,
  A ransomed soul.

R. PALMER, 1830.

86

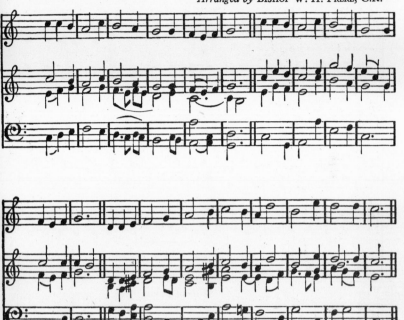

NARROW thy path, O pilgrim lone, through wilderness wide ;
Rough is the way with rock and stone, O hast thou a guide ?
    CHRIST is my Guide : the SON of GOD
    This road so steep Himself hath trod.

Hunger and thirst, O pilgrim weak, now over thee brood,
Where, in the desert bare and bleak, obtainest thou food ?
    CHRIST is my Food : He doth impart
    His Life Divine to my frail heart.

Weary thou art, O pilgrim faint, with troubles oppressed ;
Out in the wild, O lonely saint, where findest thou rest ?
    CHRIST is my Rest : His Church my home,
    And Heaven's bright Hosts to cheer me come.

Short is the day, O pilgrim frail, on cometh the night ;
Then, as the shadows deep prevail, where shalt thou find light ?
    CHRIST is my Light : and CHRIST the Way
    That leads through death to endless day.

T. REES, 1916.

87

IRREGULAR.   *Traditional Melody.*

Without pedals.

Pedals

O COME, all ye faithful,
Joyful and triumphant;
O come ye, O come ye to Bethlehem.
Come and behold Him
Born, the King of Angels;
O come, let us adore Him,
O come, let us adore Him,
O come, let us adore Him,
CHRIST the LORD.

Sing, choirs of Angels,
Sing in exultation,
Sing, all ye citizens of Heaven above:
"Glory to GOD
In the highest!"
O come, let us adore Him,
O come, let us adore Him,
O come, let us adore Him,
CHRIST the LORD.

GOD of GOD,
Light of Light,
Lo! He abhors not the Virgin's womb;
Very GOD,
Begotten, not created;
O come, let us adore Him,
O come, let us adore Him,
O come, let us adore Him,
CHRIST the LORD.

Yea, LORD, we greet Thee,
Born this happy morning;
JESU, to Thee be glory given.
Word of the FATHER,
Now in flesh appearing:
O come, let us adore Him,
O come, let us adore Him,
O come, let us adore Him,
CHRIST the LORD.

Tr. F. OAKELEY, 1841.

88

HIDING IN THEE. IRREGULAR. *Ad. from* I. D. SANKEY,
1840-1908.

(By permission of Morgan & Scott Ltd.)

O COME to the merciful SAVIOUR, Who calls you,
O come to the LORD, Who forgives and forgets;
Though dark be the fortune on earth that befalls you,
There's a bright Home above, where the sun never sets.

O come then to JESUS, Whose Arms are extended
To fold His dear children in closest embrace;
O come, for your exile will shortly be ended,
And JESUS will show you His beautiful Face.

Then come to the SAVIOUR, Whose mercy grows brighter
The longer you look at the depths of His love;
And fear not! 'tis JESUS! and life's cares grow lighter
As you think of the Home and the Glory above.

Have you sinned as none else in the world have before you
Are you blacker than all other creatures in guilt?
O fear not, and doubt not! the mother who bore you
Loves you less than the SAVIOUR Whose Blood you have spilt!

O come then to JESUS, and say how you love Him,
And swear at His feet you will keep in His Grace;
For one tear that is shed by a sinner can move Him;
And your sins will drop off in His tender embrace.

Then come to His Feet, and lay open your story
Of suffering and sorrow, of guilt and of shame!
For the pardon of sin is the crown of His glory,
And the joy of our LORD to be true to His Name.

F. W. FABER, 1854.

89

ST. COLUMBA.
(*First Tune.*)

C.M.

Ancient Irish Hymn Melody.

(*By permission of Stainer & Bell Ltd.*)

DIVINE COMPASSION.
(*Second Tune.*)

C.M.

G. W. HART, C.R., 1918.

O DEAREST LORD, Thy sacred Brow
  With thorns was pierced for me ;
O pour Thy blessing on my head,
  That I may think for Thee.

O dearest LORD, Thy sacred Hands
  With nails were pierced for me ;
O send Thy blessing on my hands,
  That they may work for Thee.

O dearest LORD, Thy sacred Feet
  With nails were pierced for me ;
O send Thy blessing on my feet,
  That they may follow Thee.

O dearest LORD, Thy sacred Heart
  With spear was pierced for me ;
O shed Thy blessing on my heart,
  That I may live for Thee.

FR. ANDREW, S.D.C., 1918.

90

BELMONT.   C.M.   S. WEBBE, Junr.

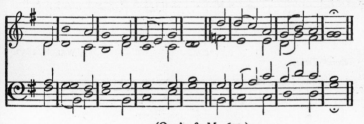

(Or A. & M. 630.)

O FOR a closer walk with GOD,
  A calm and heav'nly frame ;
A light to shine upon the road
  That leads me to the LAMB.

What peaceful hours I once enjoyed,
  How sweet their memory still !
But they have left an aching void
  The world can never fill.

Return, O Holy DOVE, return,
  Sweet Messenger of rest ;
I hate the sins that made Thee mourn,
  And drove Thee from my breast.

The dearest idol I have known,
  Whate'er that idol be,
Help me to tear it from Thy throne,
  And worship only Thee.

So shall my walk be close with GOD,
  Calm and serene my frame ;
So purer light shall mark the road
  That leads me to the Lamb.

W. COWPER, 1772.

91

BANGOR.
(*First Tune.*)   C.M.   WILLIAM TANS'UR, 1724.

SAWLEY.
(*Second Tune.*)   C.M.   J. WALCH, 1857.

O FOR a heart to praise my GOD,
  A heart from sin set free ;
A heart that's sprinkled with the Blood
  So freely shed for me ;

A heart resigned, submissive, meek,
  My great Redeemer's throne,
Where only CHRIST is heard to speak,
  Where JESUS reigns alone ;

A humble, lowly, contrite heart,
  Believing, true and clean,
Which neither life nor death can part
  From Him that dwells within ;

A heart in every thought renewed,
  And filled with love Divine,
Perfect, and right, and pure, and good,
  A copy, LORD, of Thine.

Thy nature, gracious LORD, impart ;
  Come quickly from above,
Write Thy new Name upon my heart,
  Thy new best Name of Love.

C. WESLEY, 1742.

92

LANSDOWNE.
(*First Tune.*)

C.M.

H. HARRINGTON, 1727-1816.

EVAN.
(*Second Tune.*)

C.M.

W. H. HAVERGAL, 1847.

O FOR a thousand tongues to sing
My dear Redeemer's praise !
The glories of my GOD and King,
The triumphs of His grace.

My gracious Master and my GOD,
Assist me to proclaim
And spread through all the earth abroad
The honours of Thy Name.

JESUS—the Name that charms our fears,
That bids our sorrows cease ;
'Tis music to the sinner's ears,
'Tis life, and health, and peace,

He breaks the power of cancelled sin,
He sets the prisoner free ;
His Blood can make the foulest clean,
His Blood availed for me.

He speaks ; and, listening to His Voice,
New life the dead receive ;
The mournful, broken hearts rejoice,
The humble poor believe.

Hear Him, ye deaf ; His praise, ye dumb,
Your loosened tongues employ ;
Ye blind, behold your SAVIOUR come ;
And leap, ye lame, for joy.

See all your sins on JESUS laid ;
The LAMB of GOD was slain,
His Soul was once an Offering made
For every soul of man.

C. WESLEY, 1767.

93

7.6.7.6.D.   *English Traditional Melody.*

(From the English Hymnal, by permission of the Oxford University Press.)

O GOD of earth and altar,
  Bow down and hear our cry,
Our earthly rulers falter,
  Our people drift and die ;
The walls of gold entomb us,
  The swords of scorn divide,
Take not Thy thunder from us,
  But take away our pride.

From all that terror teaches,
  From lies of tongue and pen,
From all the easy speeches
  That comfort cruel men,

From sale and profanation
  Of honour and the sword,
From sleep and from damnation,
  Deliver us, good LORD !

Tie in a living tether
  The prince and priest and thrall,
Bind all our lives together ;
  Smite us and save us all ;
In ire and exultation
  Aflame with faith, and free,
Lift up a living nation,
  A single sword to Thee.

G. K. CHESTERTON, 1906.

94

St. Anne.   C.M.   W. Croft, 1708.

O God, our help in ages past,
  Our hope for years to come,
Our shelter from the stormy blast,
  And our eternal home ;

Beneath the shadow of Thy Throne
  Thy Saints have dwelt secure ;
Sufficient is Thine Arm alone,
  And our defence is sure.

Before the hills in order stood,
  Or earth received her frame,
From everlasting Thou art God,
  To endless years the same.

A thousand ages in Thy sight
  Are like an evening gone—
Short as the watch that ends the night
  Before the rising sun.

Time, like an ever-rolling stream,
  Bears all its sons away ;
They fly forgotten, as a dream
  Dies at the opening day.

O God, our help in ages past,
  Our hope for years to come,
Be Thou our guard while troubles last,
  And our eternal home.

I. Watts, 1719.

95

WOLVERCOTE. *Unison.*   7.6.7.6.D.   W. H. FERGUSON.

O JESUS, I have promised
  To serve Thee to the end ;
Be Thou for ever near me,
  My Master and my Friend ;
I shall not fear the battle
  If Thou art by my side,
Nor wander from the pathway,
  If Thou wilt be my Guide.

O let me feel Thee near me :
  The world is ever near ;
I see the sights that dazzle,
  The tempting sounds I hear ;
My foes are ever near me,
  Around me and within ;
But, JESUS, draw Thou nearer,
  And shield my soul from sin.

O let me hear Thee speaking
  In accents clear and still,
Above the storms of passion,
  The murmurs of self-will;
O speak to reassure me,
  To hasten or control;
O speak, and make me listen,
  Thou Guardian of my soul.

O Jesus, Thou hast promisĕd
  To all who follow Thee,
That where Thou art in glory
  There shall Thy servant be;
And, Jesus, I have promised
  To serve Thee to the end;
O give me grace to follow,
  My Master and my Friend.

O let me see Thy Foot-marks,
  And in them plant mine own;
My hope to follow duly
  Is in Thy strength alone.
O guide me, call me, draw me,
  Uphold me, to the end;
And then in Heav'n receive me,
  My Saviour and my Friend.

J. E. Bode, 1869.

96

BATTYEFORD.
       6.6.6.6.
       G. W. Hart, C.R.

O Jesu, bless our homes,
  And make them like to Thine;
Be bitterness unknown,
  Bid love and kindness shine.

Let love of God be first,
  And daily prayers arise,
As once from Nazareth
  Thine own soared to the skies.

Let lowliness abound,
  That sweet humility
Of Mary's sinless heart
  Which made her dear to Thee.

Let work be bravely done,
  As Joseph toiled of old,
For Thee and Thy reward,
  Not only for earth's gold.

Then let Thy blessing bring
  Just such prosperity
As Thou shalt deem most fit
  To keep us true to Thee.

And to Thy better Home
  O bring us at the last,
To praise Thee with Thy Saints
  When earthly joys are past.

A. H. Baverstock.

WALDEGRAVE.   IRREGULAR.   S. SWIRE, 1898.

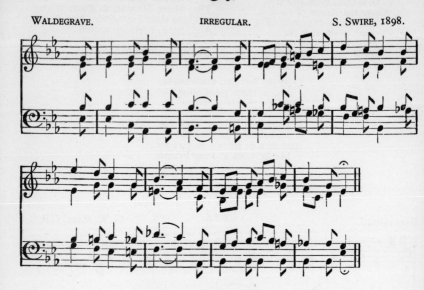

O JESUS ! GOD and Man !
  For love of children once a Child !
O JESUS ! GOD and Man !
  We hail Thee, SAVIOUR, sweet and mild.

O JESUS ! GOD and Man !
  Make us poor children dear to Thee,
And lead us to Thyself,
  To love Thee for eternity.

O JESUS ! Mary's Son !
  On Thee for grace we children call ;
Make us all men to love,
  But to love· Thee beyond them all.

O JESUS ! bless our work,
  Our sorrows soothe, our sins forgive ;
O happy, happy they
  Who in the Church of JESUS live !

O JESUS ! great and good,
  At work or play, by night or day,·
Make us remember Thee,
  Who so rememberest us alway.

F. W. FABER, 1849.

98

ST. MARGARET.
Unison.

8.8.8.8.6.

A. L. PEACE, 1885.

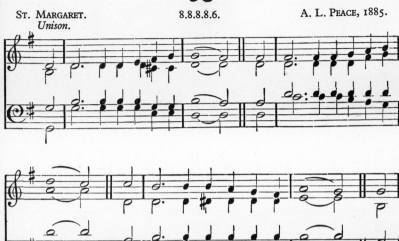

(Or A. & M. 699 [2nd] Supplement.)

O Love that wilt not let me go,
  I rest my weary soul in Thee;
I give Thee back the life I owe,
That in Thine ocean depths its flow
  May richer, fuller be.

O Light that followest all my way,
  I yield my flickering torch to
      Thee;
My heart restores its borrowed ray,
That in Thy sunshine's blaze its day
  May brighter, fairer be.

O Joy that seekest me through pain,
  I cannot close my heart to Thee;
I trace the rainbow through the rain,
And feel the promise is not vain
  That morn shall tearless be.

O Cross that liftest up my head,
  I dare not ask to fly from Thee;
I lay in dust life's glory dead,
And from the ground there blossoms
     red
  Life that shall endless be.

G. MATHESON, 1881.

(Tune and Words, by permission of Novello & Co. Ltd.)

99

NORTH COATES.   6.5.6.5.   T. R. MATTHEWS, 1862.

(By permission of Novello & Co. Ltd.)

O MY SAVIOUR, lifted
    From the earth for me,
Draw me, in Thy mercy,
    Nearer unto Thee.

Speed these lagging footsteps,
    Melt this heart of ice,
As I scan the marvels
    Of Thy Sacrifice.

Lift my earth-bound longings,
    Fix them, LORD, above ;
Draw me with the magnet
    Of Thy mighty love.

LORD, Thine Arms are stretching
    Ever far and wide,
To enfold Thy children
    To Thy loving Side.

And I come, O JESUS :—
    Dare I turn away ?
No ! Thy love hath conquered,
    And I come to-day :

Bringing all my burdens,
    Sorrow, sin, and care,
At Thy Feet I lay them,
    And I leave them there.

                    BP. W. WALSHAM HOW, 1876.

100

L.M.

H. BAKER.

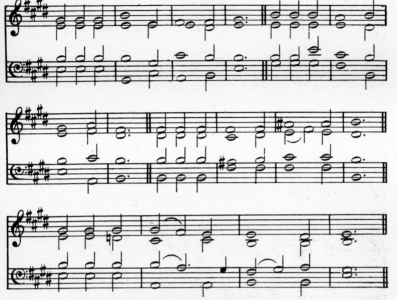

(By permission of the Editor of " Worship Song.")

O soul of Jesus, sick to death,
 Thy Blood and prayer together plead ;
My sins have bowed Thee to the ground,
 As the storm bows the feeble reed.

My God ! my God ! and can it be
 That I should sin so lightly now,
And think no more of evil thoughts
 Than of the wind that waves the bough ?

I walk the earth with lightsome step,
 Smile at the sunshine, breathe the air,
Do my own will, nor ever heed
 Gethsemane and Thy long prayer

Shall it be always thus, O Lord ?
 Wilt Thou not work this hour in me
The grace Thy passion merited,
 Hatred of self and love of Thee ?

And make me feel it was my sin,
 As though no other sins there were,
That was to Him Who bears the world
 A load that He could scarcely bear.

O, by the pains of Thy pure love,
 Grant me the gift of holy fear ;
And by Thy woes and Bloody Sweat
 O wash my guilty conscience clear.

F. W. FABER, 1849.

101

(Or Tune 5.)   (*By permission of the Royal College of Music.*)

O Thou Who makest souls to shine
  With light from lighter worlds above,
And droppest glistening dew Divine
  On all who seek a Saviour's love ;

Do Thou Thy benediction give
  On all who teach, on all who learn,
That so Thy Church may holier live,
  And every lamp more brightly burn.

Give those who teach, pure hearts and
  wise,   [prayer ;
  Faith, hope, and love, all warm'd by
Themselves first training for the skies,
  They best will raise their people
  there.

Give those who learn, the willing ear,
  The spirit meek, the guileless mind
Such gifts will make the lowliest here
  Far better than a kingdom find.

O bless the shepherd, bless the sheep,
  That guide and guided both be one
One in the faithful watch they keep,
  Until this hurrying life be done.

If thus, good Lord, Thy Grace be
  given,
  In Thee to live, in Thee to die,
Before we upward pass to Heav'n
  We taste our immortality.

Bp. J. Armstrong, 1847.

102

C.M. *Scottish Hymn Melody.*

(Or A. & M. 315.)

ONCE, only once, and once for all,
　His precious life He gave ;
Before the Cross our spirits fall
　And own it strong to save.

" One offering, single and complete,"
　With lips and heart we say ;
But what He never can repeat
　He shows forth day by day.

For, as the priest of Aaron's line
　Within the Holiest stood,
And sprinkled all the mercy-shrine
　With sacrificial blood :

So He, Who once atonement wrought,
　Our Priest of endless power,
Presents Himself for those He bought
　In that dark noontide hour.

His Manhood pleads where now It lives
　On Heaven's eternal Throne,
And where in mystic rite He gives
　Its Presence to His own.

And so we show Thy death, O LORD,
　Till Thou again appear ;
And feel, when we approach Thy Board,
　We have an Altar here.

All glory to the FATHER be,
　All glory to the SON,
All glory, HOLY GHOST, to Thee,
　While endless ages run.

W. BRIGHT, 1866.

103

HYFRYDOL.　　　　　　　　　8.7.8.7.D.　　　　　Melody by
R. H. PRICHARD, 1811-1887.

ONCE to every man and nation
  Comes the moment to decide,
In the strife of truth with falsehood,
  For the good or evil side;
Some great cause, GOD'S new MESSIAH,
  Offering each the bloom or blight—
And the choice goes by for ever
  'Twixt that darkness and that light.

Then to side with truth is noble,
  When we share her wretched crust,
Ere her cause bring fame and profit,
  And 'tis prosperous to be just;
Then it is the brave man chooses,
  While the coward stands aside,
Doubting in his abject spirit,
  Till his LORD is crucified.

By the light of burning martyrs,
  CHRIST, Thy bleeding Feet we track,
Toiling up new Calvaries ever
  With the Cross that turns not back.
New occasions teach new duties;
  Time makes ancient good uncouth;
They must upward still and onward
  Who would keep abreast of truth.

Though the cause of evil prosper,
  Yet 'tis truth alone is strong;
Though her portion be the scaffold,
  And upon the throne be wrong—
Yet that scaffold sways the future,
  And, behind the dim unknown,
Standeth GOD within the shadow,
  Keeping watch above His own.

J. RUSSELL LOWELL, 1819-1891.

104

ST. GERTRUDE.   6.5.6.5.D. and Refrain.   SIR A. SULLIVAN.

Onward, Christian sol - - diers, March-ing as to.. war,
war, With.. the
war,

126

With the Cross of JE - SUS   Go - ing on be - fore.
Cross of JE - SUS

With the Cross of JE - SUS

(By permission of Messrs. Novello & Co.)

ONWARD, Christian soldiers,
  Marching as to war,
With the Cross of JESUS
  Going on before!
CHRIST, the Royal Master,
  Leads against the foe;
Forward into battle,
  See, His banners go.

Onward, Christian soldiers,
  Marching as to war,
With the Cross of JESUS
  Going on before!

At the sign of triumph
  Satan's host doth flee!
On, then, Christian soldiers,
  On to victory!
Hell's foundations quiver
  At the shout of praise;
Brothers, lift your voices,
  Loud your anthems raise.

Like a mighty army,
  Moves the Church of GOD
Brothers, we are treading
  Where the Saints have trod;
We are not divided,
  All one Body we,
One in hope and doctrine,
  One in charity.

Crowns and thrones may perish,
  Kingdoms rise and wane,
But the Church of JESUS
  Constant will remain;
Gates of hell can never
  'Gainst that Church prevail;
We have CHRIST'S own promise,
  And that cannot fail.

Onward, then, ye people,
  Join our happy throng,
Blend with ours your voices
  In the triumph song;
Glory, praise, and honour
  Unto CHRIST the King;
This through countless ages
  Men and Angels sing.

S. BARING GOULD, 1864.

105

REFRAIN.

(By permission of Morgan & Scott Ltd.)

PASS me not, O gentle SAVIOUR,
  Hear my humble cry;
While on others Thou art calling,
  Do not pass me by.

  SAVIOUR, SAVIOUR,
    Hear my humble cry!
  And, while others Thou art calling,
    Do not pass me by.

Long, O LORD, I spurn'd Thy pleading,
  And Thy love to me;
Heard Thy Voice but lived unheeding,
  Now I turn to Thee.

Let me at the throne of mercy
  Find a sweet relief:

Kneeling there in deep contrition,
  Help my unbelief.

Trusting only in Thy merit,
  Would I seek Thy Face:
Heal my wounded, broken spirit,
  Save me by Thy Grace.

Thou the spring of all my comfort,
  More than life to me,
Whom have I on earth beside Thee?
  Whom in Heav'n but Thee?

Keep me, SAVIOUR, ever faithful
  Till I reach Thy Home;
And I hear Thy Voice so welcome
  Saying, "Blessed, come!"

                    F. J. VAN ALSTYNE, 1870.

PEACE, PEACE.   IRREGULAR.   ANON.

PEACE, peace ;
JESUS is here.
Peace, peace ;
Angels are near—
We are not left alone,
Here at His Altar Throne
Heaven and earth are one
JESUS is here.

Kneel, kneel ;
JESUS is King.
Kneel, kneel ;
Offerings bring—
Dear Babe of Bethlehem,
GOD of Jerusalem,
Love is His diadem,
JESUS is King.

Soft, soft ;
Whisper your need.
Soft, soft ;
The FATHER will heed.
Given the Holy Food,
Now as upon the Rood
Pleadeth the Precious Blood,
Whisper your need.

Rest, rest
Infinite Love.
Rest, rest ;
Here as above.
Now on His gentle Breast
Weary ones find their rest,
Truest and tenderest,
Infinite Love.

FR. ANDREW, S.D.C., 1902.

107

10.10. O. Gibbons, 1623.

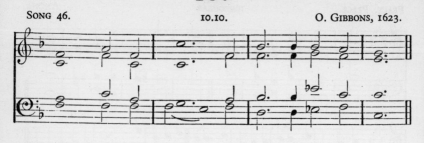

(Or A. & M. 537.)

Peace, perfect peace, in this dark world of sin?
The Blood of Jesus whispers peace within.

Peace, perfect peace, by thronging duties press'd?
To do the will of Jesus, this is rest.

Peace, perfect peace, with sorrows surging round?
On Jesus' Bosom nought but calm is found.

Peace, perfect peace, with loved ones far away?
In Jesus' keeping we are safe and they.

Peace, perfect peace, our future all unknown?
Jesus we know, and He is on the Throne.

Peace, perfect peace, death shadowing us and ours?
Jesus has vanquish'd death and all its powers.

It is enough : earth's struggles soon shall cease,
And Jesus call us to Heav'n's perfect peace.

Bp. E. H. Bickersteth. 1875.

108

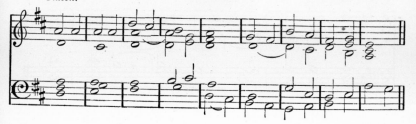

(By permission of Lady Carbery.)

PRAISE, my soul, the King of Heaven ;
To His Feet thy tribute bring ;
Ransomed, healed, restored, forgiven,
Who like thee His praise should sing ?
Praise Him ! Praise Him !
Praise the everlasting King !

Praise Him for His grace and favour
To our fathers in distress ;
Praise Him, still the same as ever,
Slow to chide, and swift to bless.
Praise Him ! Praise Him !
Glorious in His faithfulness !

Father-like He tends and spares us ;
Well our feeble frame He knows ;
In His Hands He gently bears us,
Rescues us from all our foes.
Praise Him ! Praise Him !
Widely as His mercy flows.

Angels, help us to adore Him ;
Ye behold Him face to face :
Sun and moon, bow down before Him ;
Dwellers all in time and space.
Praise Him ! Praise Him !
Praise with us the GOD of grace !

H. F. LYTE, 1834.

109

HEBDOMADAL.
(*First Tune.*)

C.M.

BP. T. B. STRONG, 1908.

GERONTIUS.
(*Second Tune.*)

(*From the Oxford Hymn-Book.*)

C.M.

J. B. DYKES, 1823-1876.

(*Or Tune 132.*)

132

PRAISE to the Holiest in the height,
   And in the depth be praise;
In all His words most wonderful,
   Most sure in all His ways.

O loving wisdom of our GOD!
   When all was sin and shame,
A second Adam to the fight
   And to the rescue came.

O wisest love! that flesh and blood,
   Which did in Adam fail,
Should strive afresh against the foe,
   Should strive, and should prevail.

And that a higher gift than grace
   Should flesh and blood refine,
GOD'S Presence and His very Self,
   And Essence all-divine.

O generous love! that He, Who smote
   In Man for man the foe,
The double agony in Man
   For man should undergo;

And in the garden secretly,
   And on the Cross on high,
Should teach His brethren, and inspire
   To suffer and to die.

Praise to the Holiest in the height,
   And in the depth be praise:
In all His words most wonderful,
   Most sure in all His ways.

                  J. H. NEWMAN, 1865.

110

ANGELS OF JESUS. IRREGULAR. *Swiss Air.*

REFRAIN.

" Quit you like men ! " Life's battle lies before you;
   Will ye prove traitors to your Prince above ?
Will ye desert His standard floating o'er you—
   The bannered Cross of JESU's dying love ?

Faithful and loyal, LORD, may we be,
   Living or dying, still faithful unto Thee,
Serving the CHRIST, and in serving Him made free.

" Quit you like men ! " Heaven's victor-voices call
      you ;
   Oh, be ashamed of all your coward shame ;
Let not the fear of man or fiend appal you,
   They always win who fight in JESU's Name.

" Quit you like men ! " No longer slaves of passion,
   Led by your lusts, or Mammon's selfish greed ;
No more enthralled by some unholy fashion,
   Freed by GOD's SON, then are ye free indeed.

" Quit you like men ! " Be true to your true nature ;
   Are not our bodies temples of our GOD ?
Grow up in CHRIST to manhood's perfect stature,
   Tread in the steps the Perfect Man hath trod.

" Quit you like men ! " " Behold the Man " that
      liveth,
   And once was slain that ye may live to GOD.
Take to your hearts th' eternal life He giveth :
   Peace, pow'r, and pardon, purchased with His
      Blood.

                              W. HAY AITKEN. 1887.

111

MEIRIONYDD. 7.6.7.6.D. *Welsh Hymn Melody.*

(Or Tune 143.)

REDEEMED, restored, forgiven
  Through JESU's precious Blood,
Heirs of His Home in Heaven,
  O praise our pardoning GOD!

Praise Him in tuneful measures
  Who gave His SON to die;
Praise Him whose sevenfold treasures
  Enrich and sanctify!

Once on the dreary mountain
  We wandered far and wide,
Far from the cleansing Fountain,
  Far from the piercèd Side;

But JESUS sought and found us
  And washed our guilt away;
With cords of love He bound us
  To be His own for aye.

Dear Master, Thine the glory
  Of each recovered soul;
Ah! who can tell the story
  Of love that made us whole?

Not ours, not ours the merit;
  Be Thine alone the praise,
And ours a thankful spirit
  To serve Thee all our days.

Now keep us, Holy SAVIOUR,
  In Thy true love and fear;
And grant us of Thy favour
  The grace to persevere;

Till, in Thy new creation,
  Earth's time-long travail o'er,
We find our full salvation,
  And praise Thee evermore.
                    H. W. BAKER, 1876.

112

ROSLYNLEE. IRREGULAR. W. H. DOANE, 1870.

(By permission of Morgan & Scott Ltd.)

RESCUE the perishing,
  Care for the dying,
Snatch them in pity from sin and the
    grave;
  Weep o'er the erring one,
  Lift up the fallen,
Tell them of JESUS, the mighty to save.

Rescue the perishing,
Care for the dying;
JESUS is merciful,
JESUS will save.

Though they are slighting Him,
  Still He is waiting,
Waiting the penitent child to receive.
  Plead with them earnestly,
  Plead with them gently;
He will forgive, if they only believe.

Down in the human heart,
  Crush'd by the tempter,
Feelings lie buried that Grace can restore;
  Touched by a loving hand,
  Wakened by kindness,
Chords that were broken will vibrate once
    more.

Rescue the perishing,
  Duty demands it;
Strength for thy labour the LORD will provide:
  Back to the narrow way
  Patiently win them;
Tell the poor wanderer a SAVIOUR has died.

F. J. VAN ALSTYNE, 1870.

113

ST. THOMAS. S.M. *Williams' Psalmody, 1770.*

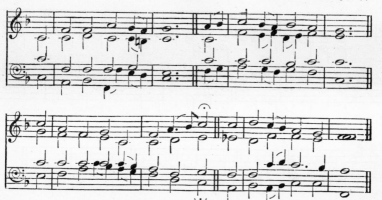

Revive Thy work, O Lord,
  Thy mighty Arm make bare;
Speak with the Voice that wakes the dead,
  And make Thy people hear.

Revive Thy work, O Lord,
  Disturb this sleep of death;
Quicken the smouldering embers now
  By Thine Almighty Breath.

Revive Thy work, O Lord,
  Create soul-thirst for Thee;
And hungering for the Bread of Life
  O may our spirits be.

Revive Thy work, O Lord,
  Exalt Thy precious Name;
And, by the Holy Ghost, our love
  For Thee and Thine inflame.

Revive Thy work, O Lord,
  And give refreshing showers;
The glory shall be all Thine own,
  The blessing, Lord, be ours!

A. MIDLANE, 1858.

114

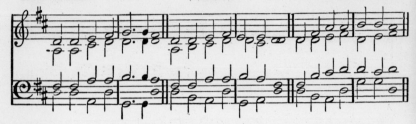

Rock of Ages, cleft for me,
Let me hide myself in Thee;
Let the Water and the Blood,
From Thy riven Side which flowed,
Be of sin the double cure,
Cleanse me from its guilt and power.

Not the labours of my hands
Can fulfil Thy law's demands;
Could my zeal no respite know,
Could my tears for ever flow,
All for sin could not atone,
Thou must save, and Thou alone.

Nothing in my hand I bring,
Simply to Thy Cross I cling:
Naked, come to Thee for dress;
Helpless, look to Thee for grace;
Foul, I to the Fountain fly;
Wash me, Saviour, or I die !

While I draw this fleeting breath,
When mine eyelids close in death,
When I soar through tracts unknown,
See Thee on Thy judgment Throne,
Rock of Ages, cleft for me,
Let me hide myself in Thee.

                                A. M. Toplady, 1775.

115

(By permission of Morgan & Scott Ltd.)

Safe in the Arms of Jesus,
  Safe on His gentle Breast,
There by His love o'ershadowed,
  Sweetly my soul shall rest.
Hark ! 'tis the voice of Angels,
  Borne in a song to me,
Over the fields of glory,
  Over the jasper sea.

Safe in the arms of Jesus,
  Safe on His gentle Breast,
There by His love o'ershadowed,
  Sweetly my soul shall rest.

Safe in the Arms of Jesus,
  Safe from corroding care,
Safe from the world's temptations,
  Sin cannot harm me there.
Free from the blight of sorrow,
  Free from my doubts and fears,
Only a few more trials,
  Only a few more tears.

Jesus, my heart's dear refuge,
  Jesus has died for me ;
Firm on the Rock of Ages
  Ever my trust shall be.
Here let me wait with patience,
  Wait till the night is o'er,
Wait till I see the morning
  Break on the golden shore.

F. J. Van Alstyne, 1869.

116

BISHOPTHORPE
(First Tune.)

C.M.

J. CLARK, 1670-1707.

SHALL WE NOT LOVE
THEE, MOTHER DEAR?
(Second Tune.)

C.M. and Refrain.

T. ADAMS.

REFRAIN.

If the tune " Bishopthorpe " is used the refrain is not sung.

SHALL we not love thee, Mother dear,
　Whom JESUS loves so well?
And to His glory, year by year,
　Thy joy and honour tell?

　　Yes, we will love thee, Mother dear,
　　Whom JESUS loves so well.

Bound with the curse of sin and shame
　We helpless sinners lay,
Until in tender love He came
　To bear the curse away.

And thee He chose from whom to take
　True flesh His Flesh to be;
In it to suffer for our sake,
　By it to make us free.

Thy Babe He lay upon thy breast,
　To thee He cried for food:
Thy gentle nursing soothed to rest
　Th' Incarnate SON of GOD.

O wondrous depth of Grace Divine
　That He should bend so low!
And Mary, O, what joy 'twas thine
　In His dear love to know.

Joy to be Mother of the LORD,
　And thine the truer bliss,
In every thought, and deed, and word,
　To be for ever His.

And as He loves thee, Mother dear,
　We too will love thee well;
And to His glory, year by year,
　Thy joy and honour tell.

JESU, the Virgin's Holy Son,
　We praise Thee and adore,
Who art with GOD the FATHER One,
　And SPIRIT evermore.

　　JESU, the Virgin's Holy Son,
　　We praise Thee and adore.

H. W. BAKER, 1868.

117

IVES.

7.7.7.7.D.

Melody from
" Plymouth Collection " (U.S.A.), 1855

SINNERS, turn ! Why will ye die ?
GOD, your Maker, asks you why—
GOD, Who did your being give,
Made you with Himself to live ;
He the fatal cause demands,
Asks the work of His own hands,
Why, ye thankless creatures, why
Will ye cross His love and die ?

Sinners, turn ! Why will ye die ?
GOD your SAVIOUR asks you why—
GOD, Who did your souls retrieve,
Died Himself that ye might live.
Will you let Him die in vain,
Crucify your LORD again ?
Why, ye ransomed sinners, why
Will ye slight His Grace and die ?

Sinners, turn ! Why will ye die ?
GOD the SPIRIT asks you why—
He Who all your lives hath strove,
Wooed you to embrace His love.
Will ye not His Grace receive ?
Will ye still refuse to live ?
Why, you long-sought sinners, why
Will you grieve your GOD and die ?

Dead already, dead within,
Spiritually dead in sin ;
Dead to GOD, while here you breathe,
Pant you after second death ?
Will ye still your sin retain ?
Will ye still in death remain ?
O, ye dying sinners, why—
Why will ye for ever die ?

C. WESLEY, 1741.

118

From Strength to Strength. D.S.M. E. W. Naylor.
(First Tune.)
C.F. 141. With vigour. Unison.

Soldiers of Christ ! arise,
　And put your armour on ;
Strong in the strength which God supplies
　Through His Eternal Son.

Strong in the Lord of Hosts,
　And in His mighty power ;
Who in the strength of Jesus trusts
　Is more than conqueror.

Stand then in His great might,
　With all His strength endued ;
And take, to arm you for the fight,
　The panoply of God.

*To keep your armour bright
　　Attend with constant care,
Still walking in your Captain's sight,
　　And watching unto prayer.

From strength to strength go on,
　　Wrestle, and fight, and pray ;
Tread all the powers of darkness down,
　　And win the well-fought day.

That having all things done,
　　And all your conflicts past,
Ye may obtain, through CHRIST alone,
　　A crown of joy at last.
　　　　　　　　　　C. WESLEY, 1748.

*If the tune "St. Ethelwald" is used this verse may be
　　　　　　　omitted.*

ST. ETHELWALD.　　　　　S.M.　　　　W. H. MONK, 1823-89.
(Second Tune.)

119

(By permission of Novello & Co. Ltd.)

(Or Tunes 28 or 103.)

SON of GOD, Eternal SAVIOUR,
  Source of life and truth and grace,
SON of Man, Whose birth incarnate
  Hallows all our human race,
Thou, our Head, Who, throned in glory,
  For Thine own dost ever plead,
Fill us with Thy love and pity,
  Heal our wrongs, and help our need.

Come, O CHRIST, and reign among us,
  King of love, and Prince of peace,
Hush the storm of strife and passion,
  Bid its cruel discords cease ;
By Thy patient years of toiling,
  By Thy silent hours of pain,
Quench our fevered thirst of pleasure,
  Shame our selfish greed of gain.

As Thou, LORD, hast lived for others,
  So may we for others live ;
Freely have Thy gifts been granted,
  Freely may Thy servants give.
Thine the gold and Thine the silver,
  Thine the wealth of land and sea,
We but stewards of Thy bounty,
  Held in solemn trust for Thee.

Ah, the past is dark behind us,
  Strewn with wrecks and stained with blood ;
But before us gleams the vision
  Of the coming brotherhood.
See the Christlike host advancing,
  High and lowly, great and small,
Linked in bonds of common service
  For the common LORD of all.

SON of GOD, eternal SAVIOUR,
  Source of life and truth and grace,
SON of Man, Whose birth incarnate,
  Hallows all our human race,
Thou Who prayest, Thou Who willest
  That Thy people should be one,
Grant, O grant our hope's fruition :
  Here on earth Thy Will be done.

                    S. C. LOWRY, 1893.

120

7.7.7.7.D.

J. PARRY, 1879.

(By permission of Hughes & Son, Publishers, Wrexham.)

Soul of Jesus, make me whole,
Meek and contrite make my soul ;
Thou most stainless Soul Divine,
Cleanse this sordid soul of mine ;
Hallow this my contrite heart,
Purify my every part :
Soul of Jesus, hallow me ;
Mercy, mercy, Lord, on me.

Save me, Body of my Lord,
Save a sinner, vile, abhorred ;
Sacred Body, wan and worn,
Bruised and mangled, scourged and torn ;
Piercèd Hands, and Feet, and Side,
Rent, insulted, crucified :
Save me—to the Cross I flee ;
Mercy, mercy, Lord, on me.

Blood of Jesus, stream of life,
Sacred stream with blessing rife,
From Thy broken Body shed
On the Cross, that Altar dread ;
Given to be our Drink Divine,
Fill my heart and make it Thine ;
Blood of Christ, my succour be ;
Mercy, mercy, Lord, on me.

Holy Water, stream that poured
From Thy riven Side, O Lord,
Wash Thou me, without, within,
Cleanse me from the taint of sin ;
Till my soul is clean and white,
Bathed, and purified, and bright
As a ransomed soul should be—
Mercy, mercy, Lord, on me.

Jesu, by the wondrous power
Of Thine awful Passion hour,
By the unimagined woe
Mortal man may never know,
By the curse upon Thee laid,
By the ransom Thou hast paid,
By Thy Passion comfort me—
Mercy, mercy, Lord, on me.

Jesu, by Thy bitter death,
By Thy last expiring breath,
Give me the eternal life,
Purchased by that mortal strife;
Thou didst suffer death that I
Might not die eternally ;
By Thy dying quicken me—
Mercy, mercy, Lord, on me.

Mercy, mercy, let me be
Never parted, Lord, from Thee
When the hour of death is near,
And my spirit faints for fear,
Call me with Thy Voice of love,
Place me near to Thee above,
With Thine Angel host to raise
An undying song of praise.

ANON.

121

LLANSANNAN.
(Second Tune.)
8.7.8.7.D.
Welsh Hymn Melody

(Or Tune 103.)

152

SOULS of men, why will ye scatter
  Like a crowd of frighten'd sheep ?
Foolish hearts ! why will ye wander
  From a love so true and deep ?
Was there ever kindest shepherd
  Half so gentle, half so sweet,
As the SAVIOUR Who would have us
  Come and gather round His Feet ?

It is GOD ! His love looks mighty,
  But is mightier than it seems ;
'Tis our FATHER, and His fondness
  Goes far out beyond our dreams.
There's a wideness in GOD's mercy,
  Like the wideness of the sea ;
There's a kindness in His justice,
  Which is more than liberty.

There is no place where earth's sorrows
  Are more felt than up in Heaven ;
There is no place where earth's failings
  Have such kindly judgment given.
There is welcome for the sinner,
  And more graces for the good ;
There is mercy with the SAVIOUR ;
  There is healing in His Blood.

There is grace enough for thousands
  Of new worlds as great as this ;
There is room for fresh creations
  In that upper home of bliss.
For the love of GOD is broader
  Than the measures of man's mind ;
And the heart of the Eternal
  Is most wonderfully kind.

Pining souls ! come nearer JESUS,
  And, O ! come not doubting thus,
But with faith that trusts more bravely
  His great tenderness for us.
If our faith were but more simple,
  We should take Him at His word ;
And our lives would be all sunshine
  In the sweetness of our LORD.

                    F. W. FABER, 1862.

122

ILFRACOMBE.   C.M.   S. WEBBE.

SPIRIT Divine, attend our prayers,
  And make our hearts Thy home ;
Descend with all Thy gracious powers,
  O come, Great SPIRIT, come !

Come as the light ; to us reveal
  Our emptiness and woe ;
And lead us in those paths of life,
  Where all the righteous go.

Come as the fire, and purge our hearts
  Like sacrificial flame ;
Let our whole soul an offering be
  To our Redeemer's Name.

Come as the dew, and sweetly bless
  This consecrated hour ;
May barrenness rejoice to own
  Thy fertilising power !

SPIRIT Divine, attend our prayers,
  Make a lost world Thy home ;
Descend with all Thy gracious powers,
  O come, Great SPIRIT, come !

                                    A. REED, 1829.

123

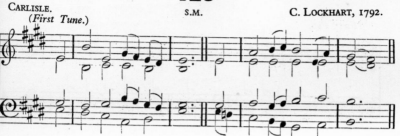

STAND up, and bless the LORD,
  Ye people of His choice;
Stand up, and bless the LORD your GOD
  With heart and soul and voice.

Though high above all praise,
  Above all blessing high,
Who would not fear His holy Name,
  And laud, and magnify?

Oh, for the living flame,
  From His own Altar brought,
To touch our lips, our minds inspire,
  And wing to Heav'n our thought!

GOD is our strength and song,
  And His salvation ours;
Then be His love in CHRIST proclaimed
  With all our ransomed powers.

Stand up, and bless the LORD;
  The LORD your GOD adore:
Stand up, and bless His glorious Name
  Henceforth for evermore.

J. MONTGOMERY, 1824.

124

MORNING LIGHT.
(First Tune.)

G. J. WEBB, 1837.

STAND UP FOR JESUS.
(Second Tune.)
In Unison.

7.6.7.6.D. and Refrain.

A. GIEBEL.

REFRAIN.
Harmony. *A tempo*.

Stand up   for JE-SUS! Ye sol-diers of the Cross! Lift high His roy-al
Stand up, stand up for JE-SUS!

ban - ner, it must not, it must not suffer   loss.

STAND up ! stand up for JESUS
  Ye soldiers of the Cross ;
Lift high His royal banner,
  It must not suffer loss.
From vict'ry unto vict'ry
  His army shall He lead,
Till every foe is vanquished,
  And CHRIST is LORD indeed.

Stand up ! for JESUS !
  Ye soldiers of the Cross ;
Lift high His royal banner,
  It must not, it must not, suffer loss.

Stand up ! stand up for JESUS !
  The trumpet call obey !
Forth to the mighty conflict
  In this His glorious day !
" Quit you like men," and serve Him
  Against unnumbered foes ;
Your courage rise with danger,
  And strength to strength oppose.

Stand up ! stand up for JESUS !
  Stand in His strength alone :
The arm of flesh will fail you,
  Ye dare not trust your own.
Put on the Gospel armour,
  And, watching unto prayer,
When duty calls, or danger,
  Be never wanting there.

Stand up ! stand up for JESUS !
  The strife will not be long ;
This day the noise of battle,
  The next the victor's song :
To him that overcometh
  A crown of life shall be !
He with the King of Glory
  Shall reign eternally.

G. DUFFIELD, 1868.

*If the tune " Morning Light " is used, the refrain is
not sung.*

125

BIRLING.
(First Tune.)

L.M. *From an early nineteenth century MS.*
Harmonised by GEOFFREY SHAW.

HURSLEY.
(Second Tune.)

L.M. KATHOLISCHES GESANGBUCH,
. c. 1774.

(Or A. M. 24 (3).)

SUN of my soul, Thou SAVIOUR dear,
It is not night if Thou be near ;
O may no earth-born cloud arise
To hide Thee from Thy servant's eyes.

When the soft dews of kindly sleep
My wearied eyelids gently steep,
Be my last thought, how sweet to rest
For ever on my SAVIOUR'S Breast.

Abide with me from morn till eve,
For without Thee I cannot live ;
Abide with me when night is nigh,
For without Thee I dare not die.

If some poor wandering child of Thine
Have spurn'd to-day the Voice Divine,
Now, LORD, the gracious work begin ;
Let him no more lie down in sin.

Watch by the sick, enrich the poor
With blessings from Thy boundless store
Be every mourner's sleep to-night
Like infants' slumbers, pure and light.

Come near and bless us when we wake,
Ere through the world our way we take ;
Till in the ocean of Thy love
We lose ourselves in Heaven above.

J. KEBLE, 1827.

126

7.7.7.7. *From* MOZART.

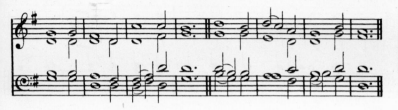

TAKE my life, and let it be
Consecrated, LORD, to Thee;
Take my moments and my days,
Let them flow in ceaseless praise.

Take my hands, and let them move
At the impulse of Thy love;
Take my feet, and let them be
Swift and beautiful for Thee.

Take my voice, and let me sing
Always, only, for my King;
Take my lips, and let them be
Filled with messages from Thee.

Take my silver and my gold,
Not a mite would I withhold;
Take my intellect, and use
Every power as Thou shalt choose.

Take my heart, it is Thine own,
It shall be Thy royal Throne;
Take my will, and make it Thine,
It shall be no longer mine.

Take my love; my LORD, I pour
At Thy Feet its treasure-store;
Take myself, and I will be
Ever, only, all for Thee.

F. R. HAVERGAL, 1878.

127

(By permission of Morgan & Scott Ltd.)

TELL me the old, old story
   Of unseen things above,
Of JESUS and His glory,
   Of JESUS and His love.
Tell me the story simply,
   As to a little child,
For I am weak and weary,
   And helpless and defil'd.

Tell me the old, old story,
  Tell me the old, old story,
Tell me the old, old story,
  Of JESUS and His love.

Tell me the story slowly,
   That I may take it in—
That wonderful redemption,
   GOD's remedy for sin.
Tell me the story often,
   For I forget so soon ;
The " early dew " of morning
   Has passed away at noon.

Tell me the story softly,
   With earnest tones and grave ;
Remember, I'm the sinner
   Whom JESUS came to save.
Tell me the story always,
   If you would really be,
In any time of trouble
   A comforter to me.

Tell me the same old story,
   When you have cause to fear
That this world's empty glory
   Is costing me too dear :
Yes, and when that world's glory
   Is dawning on my soul,
Tell me the old, old story :
   " CHRIST JESUS makes thee whole."

K. HANKEY, 1866.

UNIVERSITY. c.m. C. COLLIGNON, 1794.

(Or Tune 132 ; or English Hymnal 488.)

THE Church of GOD a kingdom is,
  Where CHRIST in power doth reign ;
Where spirits yearn till, seen in bliss,
  Their LORD shall come again.

Glad companies of saints possess
  This Church below, above :
And GOD's perpetual calm doth bless
  Their paradise of love.

An Altar stands within the shrine
  Whereon, once sacrificed,
Is set, Immaculate, Divine,
  The LAMB of GOD, the CHRIST.

There rich and poor, from countless lands,
  Praise GOD on mystic Rood ;
There nations reach forth holy hands
  To take GOD's holy Food.

There pure life-giving streams o'erflow
  The sower's garden-ground :
And faith and hope fair blossoms show,
  And fruits of love abound.

O King, O CHRIST, this endless Grace
  To us and all men bring,
To see the Vision of Thy Face
  In joy, O CHRIST, our KING.

L. MUIRHEAD.

129

AURELIA. 7.6.7.6.D. S. S. WESLEY, 1864.

THE Church's one foundation
  Is JESUS CHRIST her LORD ;
She is His new creation
  By water and the Word :
From Heav'n He came and sought her
  To be His holy Bride ;
With His own Blood He bought her,
  And for her life He died.

Elect from every nation,
  Yet one o'er all the earth,
Her charter of salvation
  One LORD, one Faith, one Birth.
One Holy Name she blesses,
  Partakes one Holy Food,
And to one hope she presses
  With every grace endued.

Though with a scornful wonder
  Men see her sore opprest,
By schisms rent‧asunder,
  By heresies distrest,
Yet Saints their watch are keeping,
  Their cry goes up : " How long ? "
And soon the night of weeping
  Shall be the morn of song.

'Mid toil and tribulation,
  And tumult of her war,
She waits the consummation
  Of peace for evermore ;
Till with the Vision glorious
  Her longing eyes are blest,
And the great Church victorious
  Shall be the Church at rest.

Yet she on earth hath union
  With GOD the THREE in ONE,
And mystic sweet communion
  With those whose rest is won :
O happy ones and holy !
  LORD, give us grace that we,
Like them the meek and lowly,
  On high may dwell with Thee.

S. J. STONE, 1866.

163

130

The Head that once was crown'd with thorns
　　Is crown'd with glory now ;
A royal diadem adorns
　　The mighty Victor's Brow.

The highest place that Heaven affords
　　Is His, is His by right,
The King of kings and Lord of lords,
　　And Heaven's eternal Light.

The joy of all who dwell above,
　　The joy of all below,
To whom He manifests His love
　　And grants His Name to know.

To them the Cross, with all its shame,
　　With all its grace, is given ;
Their name, an everlasting name,
　　Their joy, the joy of Heaven.

They suffer with their Lord below,
　　They reign with Him above ;
Their profit and their joy to know
　　The mystery of His love.

To them the Cross is life and health,
　　Though shame and death to Him ;
His people's hope, His people's wealth,
　　Their everlasting theme.

T. Kelly, 1820.

131

SKERTON.   7.6.7.6.D.   *English Traditional Melody.*

REFRAIN.

THE Saints all crowned with glory,
 In Heaven's eternal day,
To JESUS our Redeemer,
 For our salvation pray.

The Saints our dearest brothers,
 Who now with JESUS dwell,
Are by the world derided,
 But we will love them well.

We love that sacred Virgin,
 The Mother of our GOD ;
We love the LORD's Apostles,
 Who in His footsteps trod.

We love the noble Martyrs,
 The Virgin choir we love ;
The Matrons and Confessors,
 And all the Saints above.

Then, JESUS, let Thy Mother
 And all the Saints entreat
That we may share their glory,
 And worship at Thy Feet.

ANON.

165

132

C.M. *Adapted from* T. Haweis, 1734-1820
By S. Webbe (the Younger).

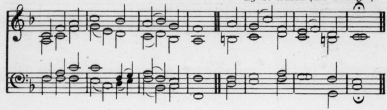

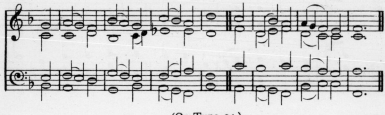

(Or Tune 94.)

(A higher setting will be found at No. 181.)

The Son of God goes forth to war,
A kingly crown to gain;
His blood-red banner streams afar;
Who follows in His train?

A glorious band, the chosen few
On whom the Spirit came,
Twelve valiant Saints, their hope they knew,
And mock'd the cross and flame.

Who best can drink his cup of woe,
Triumphant over pain,
Who patient bears his cross below,
He follows in His train.

They met the tyrant's brandish'd steel,
The lion's gory mane,
They bow'd their necks, the death to feel;
Who follows in their train?

The Martyr first, whose eagle eye
Could pierce beyond the grave;
Who saw his Master in the sky,
And call'd on Him to save.

A noble army, men and boys,
The matron and the maid,
Around the Saviour's Throne rejoice
In robes of light array'd.

Like Him, with pardon on his tongue
In midst of mortal pain,
He pray'd for them that did the wrong;
Who follows in his train?

They climb'd the steep ascent of Heav'n
Through peril, toil and pain;
O God, to us may grace be given
To follow in their train.

R. Heber, 1827.

133

WILTSHIRE.   C.M.   G. SMART, 1795.

THERE is a fountain fill'd with Blood,
  Drawn from EMMANUEL'S veins,
And sinners, plung'd beneath that flood,
  Lose all their guilty stains.

The dying thief rejoiced to see
  That fountain in his day;
And there may I, though vile as he,
  Wash all my sins away.

Dear dying LAMB, Thy precious Blood
  Shall never lose its power,
Till all the ransomed Church of GOD
  Be saved, to sin no more.

E'er since by faith I saw the stream
  Thy flowing wounds supply,
Redeeming love has been my theme,
  And shall be till I die.

Then in a nobler, sweeter song,
  I'll sing Thy power to save,
When this poor lisping, stammering tongue
  Lies silent in the grave.

W. COWPER, 1772.

134

HORSLEY.
(First Tune.)   C.M.   W. HORSLEY, 1844.

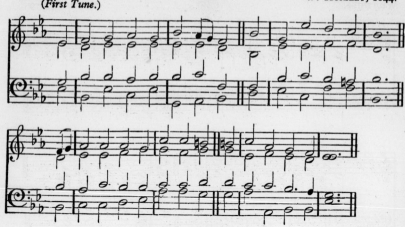

THERE is a green hill far away,
  Outside a city wall,
Where the dear LORD was crucified,
  Who died to save us all.

Oh, dearly, dearly has He loved,
  And we must love Him too,
And trust in His redeeming Blood,
  And try His works to do.

We may not know, we cannot tell,
  What pains He had to bear,
But we believe it was for us
  He hung and suffer'd there.

He died that we might be forgiven,
  He died to make us good,
That we might go at last to Heav'n,
  Saved by His precious Blood.

There was no other good enough
  To pay the price of sin.
He only could unlock the gate
  Of Heav'n, and let us in.

                    C. F. ALEXANDER, 1848.

If the tune " Horsley " is used, the Refrain is sung only
            after the last verse.

134

(*Second Tune.*)   c.m. and Refrain.   ANON.

REFRAIN.

Oh, dear - ly, dearly has He loved, And   we must love Him too,

And   trust   in His   re – deem-ing Blood, And   try His works to   do.

135

(By permission of Morgan & Scott Ltd.)

* The last line in each verse is repeated, and the crotchets marked with an asterisk are omitted in verse 3.

There were ninety and nine that safely lay
　　In the shelter of the fold,
But one was out on the hills away,
　　Far off from the gates of gold ;
Away on the mountains wild and bare,
Far from the tender Shepherd's care.

" Lord, hast Thou not here Thy ninety and nine ;
　　Are they not enough for Thee ? "
But the Shepherd made answer : " This of Mine
　　Has wandered away from Me ;
And although the road be rough and steep,
I go to the mountain to find My sheep."

But none of the ransomed ever knew
  How deep were the waters crossed;
Nor how dark was the night that the Lord passed
    through
  Ere He found His sheep that was lost.
Out in the desert He heard its cry—
Faint and weary, and ready to die.

"Lord, whence are those blood-drops all the way
  That mark out the mountain's track?"
"They were shed for one who had gone astray
  Ere the Shepherd could bring him back."
"Lord, whence are Thy Hands so rent and torn?"
"They are pierced to-night by many a thorn."

And all through the mountains, thunder-riven,
  And up from the rocky steep,
There rose a cry to the gate of Heaven,
  "Rejoice! I have found My sheep!"
And the Angels echoed around the Throne,
"Rejoice, for the Lord brings back His own!"

E. C. Clephane, 1874.

136

NEWINGTON.   7.7.7.7.   ARCHBISHOP MACLAGAN, 1875.

Thine for ever! God of love,
Hear us from Thy Throne above;
Thine for ever may we be
Here and in eternity.

Thine for ever! oh, how blest
They who find in Thee their rest!
Saviour, Guardian, Heavenly Friend,
O defend us to the end.

Thine for ever! Lord of life,
Shield us through our earthly strife;
Thou the Life, the Truth, the Way,
Guide us to the realms of day.

Thine for ever! Shepherd, keep
These Thy frail and trembling sheep;
Safe alone beneath Thy care,
Let us all Thy goodness share.

Thine for ever! Thou our Guide,
All our wants by Thee supplied,
All our sins by Thee forgiven,
Lead us, Lord, from earth to Heav'n.

M. F. Maude, 1848.

137

(Or Tune 178.)

Think, O Lord, in mercy
　On the souls of those
Who, in faith gone from us,
　Now in death repose.
Here 'mid stress and conflict
　Toils can never cease ;
There, the warfare ended,
　Bid them rest in peace.

Often were they wounded
　In the deadly strife ;
Heal them, good Physician,
　With the balm of life.
Every taint of evil,
　Frailty and decay,
Good and gracious Saviour,
　Cleanse and purge away.

Rest eternal grant them,
　After weary fight ;
Shed on them the radiance
　Of Thy heav'nly light ;
Lead them onward, upward,
　To the holy place,
Where Thy Saints made perfect
　Gaze upon Thy Face.

E. S. Palmer, 1901.

138

MARGARET.   IRREGULAR.   T. R. MATTHEWS, 1876.

REFRAIN.

(By permission of Novello & Co. Ltd.)

THOU didst leave Thy Throne and Thy kingly Crown,
  When Thou camest to earth for me ;
But in Bethlehem's home was there found no room
  For Thy holy Nativity :
    O come to my heart, LORD JESUS,
    There is room in my heart for Thee.

Heaven's arches rang when the Angels sang,
  Proclaiming Thy royal degree ;
But in lowly birth didst Thou come to earth,
  And in great humility :

The foxes found rest, and the bird had its nest
  In the shade of the cedar tree ;
But Thy couch was the sod, O THOU SON OF GOD,
  In the desert of Galilee :

Thou camest, O LORD, with the living Word
  That should set Thy people free ;
But with mocking scorn, and with crown of thorn,
  They bore Thee to Calvary :

When the heavens shall ring, and the Angels sing
  At Thy coming to victory,
Let Thy Voice call me home, saying : " Yet there is
  room—
  There is room at My Side for thee ".   E. E. S. ELLIOTT, 1864.

139

SACRAMENTUM UNITATIS.   10.10.10.10.10.10.   C. H. LLOYD, 1889.

(Or Tune 6.)   *(By permission of the Proprietors of Hymns A. & M.)*

THOU, Who at Thy first Eucharist didst pray
    That all Thy Church might be for ever one,
Grant us at every Eucharist to say,
    With longing heart and soul, " Thy will be done."
O may we all one Bread, one Body be,
Through this blest Sacrament of Unity !

For all Thy Church, O LORD, we intercede ;
    Make Thou our sad divisions soon to cease.
Draw us the nearer each to each, we plead,
    By drawing all to Thee, O Prince of Peace :
Thus may we all one Bread, one Body be,
Through this blest Sacrament of Unity.

We pray Thee, too, for wanderers from Thy fold :
    O bring them back, Good Shepherd of the sheep—
Back to the Faith which Saints believed of old,
    Back to the Church which still that Faith doth keep :
Soon may we all one Bread, one Body be,
Through this blest Sacrament of Unity.

So, LORD, at length when Sacraments shall cease,
    May we be one with all Thy Church above.
One with Thy Saints in one unbroken peace,
    One with Thy Saints in one unbounded love :
More blessèd still, in peace and love to be
One with the TRINITY in UNITY.   W. H. TURTON, 1881.

140

MARCHING.   8.7.8.7.   MARTIN SHAW.

(By permission, from Curwen Edition, No. 6300, published by J. Curwen & Sons Ltd., 24, Berners Street, London, W.1.)

(Or Tunes 63 or 119.)

THROUGH the night of doubt and sorrow
   Onward goes the pilgrim band,
Singing songs of expectation,
   Marching to the Promised Land.

Clear before us through the darkness
   Gleams and burns the guiding Light;
Brother clasps the hand of brother,
   Stepping fearless through the night.

One the light of GOD's own Presence
   O'er His ransomed people shed,
Chasing far the gloom and terror,
   Brightening all the path we tread.

One the object of our journey,
   One the faith which never tires,
One the earnest looking forward,
   One the hope our GOD inspires.

One the strain that lips of thousands
   Lift as from the heart of one;
One the conflict, one the peril,
   One the march in GOD begun:

One the gladness of rejoicing
   On the far eternal shore,
Where the One Almighty FATHER
   Reigns in love for evermore.

Onward, therefore, pilgrim brothers,
   Onward with the Cross our aid;
Bear its shame, and fight its battle,
   Till we rest beneath its shade.

Soon shall come the great awaking,
   Soon the rending of the tomb;
Then the scattering of all shadows,
   And the end of toil and gloom.

                  S. BARING GOULD, 1867.

141

THORNBURY.   7.6.7.6.D.   B. HARWOOD.

With dignity.   *Unison.*

THY Hand, O GOD, has guided
   Thy flock, from age to age ;
The wondrous tale is written,
   Full clear, on every page ;
Our fathers own'd Thy goodness,
   And we their deeds record ;
And both of this bear witness,
   One Church, one Faith, one LORD.

Thy heralds brought glad tidings
   To greatest, as to least ;
They bade men rise, and hasten
   To share the great King's feast ;
And this was all their teaching,
   In every deed and word,
To all alike proclaiming
   One Church, one Faith, one LORD.

When shadows thick were falling,
   And all seem'd sunk in night,
Thou, LORD, didst send Thy servants,
   Thy chosen sons of light.
On them and on Thy people
   Thy plenteous Grace was pour'd,
And this was still their message,
   One Church, one Faith, one LORD.

Through many a day of darkness,
   Through many a scene of strife,
The faithful few fought bravely
   To guard the nation's life.
Their Gospel of redemption,
   Sin pardoned, man restored,
Was all in this enfolded,
   One Church, one Faith, one LORD.

And we, shall we be faithless ?
   Shall hearts fail, hands hang down ?
Shall we evade the conflict,
   And cast away our crown ?
Not so : in GOD'S deep counsels
   Some better thing is stored ;
We will maintain, unflinching,
   One Church, one Faith, one LORD.

Thy mercy will not fail us,
   Nor leave Thy work undone ;
With Thy right Hand to help us,
   The victory shall be won ;
And then, by men and Angels,
   Thy Name shall be adored,
And this shall be their anthem,
   One Church, one Faith, one LORD.

E. H. PLUMPTRE, 1886.

142

St. Cecilia.   6.6.6.6.   L. G. Hayne, 1863.

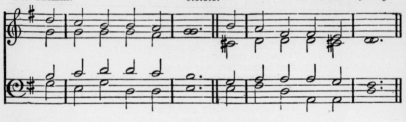

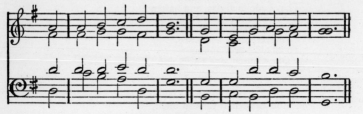

Thy kingdom come, O God,
   Thy rule, O Christ, begin;
Break with Thine iron rod
   The tyrannies of sin.

Where is Thy reign of peace,
   And purity, and love?
When shall all hatred cease,
   As in the realms above?

When comes the promised time
   That war shall be no more,
And lust oppression, crime,
   Shall flee Thy Face before?

We pray Thee, Lord, arise,
   And come in Thy great might;
Revive our longing eyes,
   Which languish for Thy sight.

Men scorn Thy sacred Name,
   And wolves devour Thy fold;
By many deeds of shame
   We learn that love grows cold.

O'er heathen lands afar
   Thick darkness broodeth yet;
Arise, O morning Star,
   Arise, and never set.

L. Hensley, 1867.

143

7.6.7.6.D.

Melody by
LOWELL MASON, 1792-1872.

TO-DAY Thy mercy calls us
  To wash away our sin,
However great our trespass,
  Whatever we have been ;
However long from mercy
  Our hearts have turned away,
Thy precious Blood can cleanse us,
  And make us white to-day.

To-day our FATHER calls us,
  His HOLY SPIRIT waits ;
His blesséd Angels gather
  Around the heavenly gates ;
No question will be asked us
  How often we have come ;
Although we oft have wandered,
  It is our FATHER'S Home.

To-day Thy gate is open,
  And all who enter in
Shall find a FATHER'S welcome,
  And pardon for their sin.
The past shall be forgotten,
  A present joy be given,
A future grace be promised,
  A glorious crown in Heaven.

O all-embracing mercy !
  O ever-open door !
What should we do without Thee,
  When heart and eye run o'er ?
When all things seem against us,
  To drive us to despair,
We know one Gate is open,
  One Ear will hear our prayer.

O. ALLEN, 1861.

144

(Or Tune 31.)

I

Weary of earth and laden with my sin,
I look at Heaven and long to enter in ;
But there no evil thing may find a home,
And yet I hear a Voice that bids me " Come."

So vile I am, how dare I hope to stand
In the pure glory of that holy Land ?
Before the whiteness of that Throne appear ?
Yet there are Hands stretch'd out to draw me near.

The while I fain would tread the heavenly way,
Evil is ever with me day by day ;
Yet on mine ears the gracious tidings fall :
" Repent, confess, thou shalt be loosed from all."

It is the Voice of Jesus that I hear,
His are the Hands stretched out to draw me near,
And His the Blood that can for all atone,
And set me faultless there before the Throne.

'Twas He Who found me on the deathly wild,
And made me heir of Heaven, the Father's child,
And day by day, whereby my soul may live,
Gives me His grace of pardon, and will give.

II

O great Absolver, grant my soul may wear
The lowliest garb of penitence and prayer,
That in the Father's courts my glorious dress
May be the garment of Thy righteousness.

Yea, Thou wilt answer for me, righteous Lord—
Thine all the merits, mine the great reward ;
Thine the sharp thorns, and mine the golden crown;
Mine the life won, and Thine the life laid down.

Nought can I bring, dear Lord, for all I owe,
Yet let my full heart what it can bestow ;
Like Mary's gift let my devotion prove,
Forgiven greatly, how I greatly love.

S. J. Stone, 1866.

145

(By permission of Morgan & Scott Ltd.)

WHAT a friend we have in JESUS,
   All our sins and grief to bear ;
What a privilege to carry
   Everything to GOD in prayer !
Oh, what peace we often forfeit,
   Oh, what needless pain we bear,
All because we do not carry
   Everything to GOD in prayer.

Have we trials and temptations ?
   Is there trouble anywhere ?
We should never be discouraged ;
   Take it to the LORD in prayer.
Can we find a friend so faithful,
   Who will all our sorrows share ?
JESUS knows our every weakness ;
   Take it to the LORD in prayer.

Are we weak and heavy-laden,
   Cumbered with a load of care ?
Rest on Him thy spirit's burden,
   Take it to the LORD in prayer.
Do thy friends despise, forsake thee ?
   Take it to the LORD in prayer ;
In His Arms He'll take and shield thee,
   Thou wilt find thy solace there.

J. SCRIVEN, 1857.

146

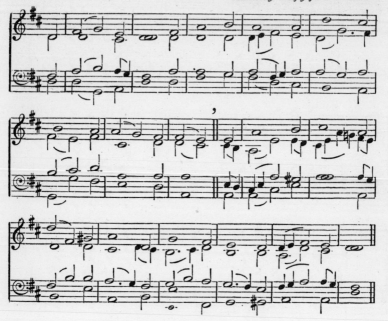

ROCKINGHAM.   L.M.   *Adapted by* E. MILLER, 1731-1807.
Harmony chiefly from S. WEBBE.

WHEN I survey the wondrous Cross,
 On which the Prince of Glory died,
My richest gain I count but loss,
 And pour contempt on all my pride.

Forbid it, LORD, that I should boast
 Save in the death of CHRIST my GOD ;
All the vain things that charm me most,
 I sacrifice them to His Blood.

See from His Head, His Hands, His Feet,
 Sorrow and love flow mingled down ;
Did e'er such love and sorrow meet,
 Or thorns compose so rich a crown ?

His dying crimson like a robe,
 Spreads o'er His Body on the Tree ;
Then am I dead to all the globe,
 And all the globe is dead to me.

Were the whole realm of nature mine,
 That were a present far too small ;
Love so amazing, so divine,
 Demands my soul, my life, my all.

       I. WATTS, 1707.

COUNT YOUR BLESSINGS.

E. O. EXCELL..

WHEN upon life's billows you are tempest-tossed,
When you are discouraged thinking all is lost,
Count your many blessings, name them one by one,
And it will surprise you what the LORD hath done.

Count your blessings, name them one by one,
Count your blessings, see what GOD hath done ;
Count your blessings, name them one by one,
And it will surprise you what the LORD hath done.

Are you ever burdened with a load of care ?
Does the cross seem heavy you are called to bear ?
Count your many blessings, every doubt will fly,
And you will be singing as the days go by.

When you look at others with their lands and gold,
Think that CHRIST has promised you His wealth un-
    told ;
Count your many blessings ; money cannot buy
Your reward in Heaven, nor your home on high.

So, amid the conflict, whether great or small,
Do not be discouraged, GOD is over all ;
Count your many blessings, Angels will attend,
Help and comfort give you to your journey's end.

J. OATMAN.

148

WHO are these like stars appearing,
  These, before GOD's Throne who stand?
Each a golden crown is wearing,
  Who are all this glorious band?
    Alleluia, hark! they sing,
    Praising loud their heavenly King.

Who are these in dazzling brightness,
  Clothed in GOD's own righteousness?
These, whose robes of purest whiteness
  Shall their lustre still possess,
    Still untouch'd by time's rude hand;—
    Whence came all this glorious band?

These are they who have contended
  For their SAVIOUR's honour long,
Wrestling on till life was ended,
  Following not the sinful throng;
    These, who well the fight sustain'd,
    Triumph by the LAMB have gain'd.

These are they whose hearts were riven,
  Sore with woe and anguish tried,
Who in prayer full oft have striven
  With the GOD they glorified;
    Now, their painful conflict o'er,
    GOD has bid them weep no more.

These, the ALMIGHTY contemplating,
  Did as priests before Him stand,
Soul and body always waiting
  Day and night at His command:
    Now in GOD's most holy place
    Blest they stand before His Face.

Tr. F. E. COX, 1841.

149

Crown Him, crown Him, crown Him, crown Him, crown Him, LORD of all.

WHO is He, in yonder stall,
At Whose Feet the shepherds fall ?

    'Tis the LORD! O wondrous story !
    'Tis the LORD, the King of Glory !
      At His Feet we humbly fall ;
      Crown Him, crown Him LORD of all !
    At His Feet we humbly fall—the LORD of
    * all :*
    Crown Him, LORD of all !

Who is He, in yonder cot,
Bending to His toilsome lot ?

Who is He, in deep distress,
Fasting in the wilderness ?

Who is He that stands and weeps
At the grave where Lazarus sleeps

Lo! at midnight, Who is He,
Prays in dark Gethsemane ?

Who is He, in Calvary's throes,
Asks for blessings on His foes ?

Who is He that from the grave
Comes to heal and help and save ?

Who is He that on yon Throne
Rules the world of light alone ?

           B. R. HANBY, 1866.

150

HERMAS.   6.5.6.5.D. and Refrain.   F. R. HAVERGAL, 1871

(By permission of Nisbet & Co.)

WHO is on the LORD's side?
  Who will serve the King?
Who will be His helpers
  Other lives to bring?
Who will leave the world's side?
  Who will face the foe?
Who is on the LORD's side?
  Who for Him will go?
    By Thy call of mercy,
      By Thy Grace Divine,
    We are on the LORD's side;
    SAVIOUR, we are Thine.

Fierce may be the conflict,
  Strong may be the foe,
But the King's own army
  None can overthrow.
Round His standard ranging,
  Victory is secure,
For His truth unchanging
  Makes the triumph sure.
    Joyfully enlisting
      By Thy Grace Divine,
    We are on the LORD's side,
    SAVIOUR, we are Thine.

JESUS, Thou hast bought us,
  Not with gold or gem,
But with Thine own Life Blood,
  For Thy diadem.
With Thy blessing filling
  Each who comes to Thee,
Thou hast made us willing,
  Thou hast made us free.
    By Thy great redemption,
      By Thy Grace Divine,
    We are on the LORD's side;
    SAVIOUR, we are Thine.

Chosen to be soldiers
  In an alien land,
Chosen, called, and faithful,
  For our Captain's band;
In the service royal
  Let us not grow cold;
Let us be right loyal,
  Noble, true, and bold.
    Master, Thou wilt keep us,
      By Thy Grace Divine,
    Always on the LORD's side,
    SAVIOUR, always Thine.

          F. R. HAVERGAL, 1877.

151

VIOLS. 11.12 and Refrain. P. BLISS, 1838-76.

REFRAIN.

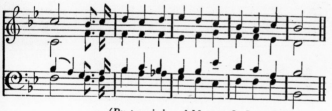

(*By permission of Morgan & Scott Ltd.*)

WITH harps and with viols there stand a great throng,
In the presence of JESUS and sing this new song:

"*Unto Him Who hath loved us and washed us from sin,*
Unto Him be the glory for ever, Amen."

All these once were sinners, defiled in His sight,
Now arrayed in pure garments in praise they unite.

He maketh the rebel a priest and a king,
He hath bought us, and taught us this new song to sing.

How helpless and hopeless we sinners had been,
If He never had loved us till cleansed from our sin.

Alone in His praises our voices shall ring,
So that others believing this new song shall sing.

A. T. PIERSON, 1886.

152

Unison.

Harmony.

Unison.

Harmony.   Unison.

Al - le - lu - ia, Al - le - lu - ia, Al - le - lu - ia, Al - le -

- lu - ia,   Al - le - lu - - - ia.

Yᴇ Watchers and ye Holy Ones,
Bright Seraphs, Cherubim and Thrones,
　Raise the glad strain, Alleluia!
Cry out Dominions, Princedoms, Powers,
Virtues, Archangels, Angels' choirs,
　Alleluia, Alleluia, Alleluia, Alleluia, Alleluia!

O higher than the Cherubim,
More glorious than the Seraphim,
　Lead their praises, Alleluia!
Thou Bearer of the eternal Word,
Most gracious, magnify the Lᴏʀᴅ,
　Alleluia, Alleluia, Alleluia, Alleluia, Alleluia!

Respond, ye souls in endless rest,
Ye Patriarchs and Prophets blest,
　Alleluia, Alleluia!
Ye holy Twelve, ye Martyrs strong,
All Saints triumphant, raise the song,
　Alleluia, Alleluia, Alleluia, Alleluia, Alleluia!

O friends, in gladness let us sing,
Supernal anthems echoing,
　Alleluia, Alleluia!
To Gᴏᴅ the Fᴀᴛʜᴇʀ, Gᴏᴅ the Sᴏɴ,
And Gᴏᴅ the Sᴘɪʀɪᴛ, Tʜʀᴇᴇ in Oɴᴇ,
　Alleluia, Alleluia, Alleluia, Alleluia, Alleluia!

A. Rɪʟᴇʏ, 1906.

153

S. Barnabas, Oxford.   8.7.8.7.D.   Claude Williams.

Hail Mary Hail Mary Hail Mary full of grace.

(Or Tune 22.)

YE who own the faith of JESUS,
  Sing the wonders that were done,
When the love of GOD the FATHER
  O'er our sin the victory won,
When He made the Virgin Mary
  Mother of His only SON.
    Hail, Mary, full of grace.

Blessèd were the chosen people
  Out of whom the LORD did come,
Blessèd was the land of promise
  Fashioned for His earthly home;
But more blessèd far the Mother,
  She who bare Him in her womb.

Wherefore let all faithful people
  Tell the honour of her name,
Let the Church in her foreshadowed
  Part in her thanksgiving claim;
What CHRIST'S Mother sang in gladness
  Let CHRIST'S people sing the same.

Let us weave our supplications,
  She with us and we with her,
For th' advancement of the faithful,
  For each faithful worshipper,
For the doubting, for the sinful,
  For each heedless wanderer.

May the Mother's intercessions
  On our homes a blessing win,
That the children all be prospered,
  Strong and fair and pure within,
Following our LORD'S own footsteps,
  Firm in faith and free from sin.

For the sick and for the agèd,
  For our dear ones far away,
For the hearts that mourn in secret,
  All who need our prayers to-day,
For the faithful gone before us,
  May the holy Virgin pray.

Praise, O Mary, praise the FATHER,
  Praise thy SAVIOUR and thy SON,
Praise the everlasting SPIRIT,
  Who hath made thee ark and throne,
O'er all creatures high exalted,
  Lowly praise the THREE in ONE.
                V. S. S. COLES, 1845-1929.

154

FORTITUDE. IRREGULAR. H. R. PALMER, 1868.

REFRAIN.

(Or Tune 84.)

YIELD not to temptation, for yielding is sin,
Each vict'ry will help you some other to win ;
Fight manfully onward, dark passions subdue,
Look ever to JESUS : He will carry you through.

Ask the SAVIOUR to help you,
Comfort, strengthen and keep you ;
He is willing to aid you :
He will carry you through.

Shun evil companions, bad language disdain.
GOD's Name hold in reverence, nor take it in vain ;
Be thoughtful and earnest, kind-hearted and true,
Look ever to JESUS : He will carry you through.

To him that o'ercometh GOD giveth a crown ;
Through faith we shall conquer, though often cast
    down.
Our LORD and our SAVIOUR our strength will renew,
Look ever to JESUS : He will carry you through.

H. R. PALMER, 1868.

LONDON TOWN.　　　　　　7.7.7.6.　　　　　　ANON.

I.

God the FATHER, God the SON,
God the SPIRIT, THREE in ONE,
See us kneeling at Thy Throne;
　Hear us, Holy TRINITY.

JESU, Who a little child,
Born of Mary undefiled,
God and man hast reconciled;
　Hear us, Holy JESU.

JESU, in a stable born,
On that wintry Christmas morn,
To the world a mark for scorn;
　Hear us, Holy JESU.

JESU, Whom in midnight sky,
Angels welcomed with the cry,
"Glory be to God on high!"
　Hear us, Holy JESU.

JESU, Whom the shepherds greet,
Kneeling at Thine Infant Feet,
Finding there God's mercy-seat;
　Hear us, Holy JESU.

JESU, Whom the wise men sought,
And their richest offerings brought,
By a star divinely taught;
　Hear us, Holy JESU.

JESU, Who didst deign to flee,
In Thy earliest infancy,
From King Herod's cruelty;
　Hear us, Holy JESU.

JESU, Who didst all things make,
Yet obeyedst, for our sake,
Her whose nature Thou didst take;
　Hear us, Holy JESU.

JESU, Who hadst here to bear
Human sorrow, human care,
That Thou mightest with us share;
　Hear us, Holy JESU.

II.

From all vanity and pride,
Falsehoods told, and truth denied,
And from seeking faults to hide,
　Keep us, Holy JESU.

From much care for outward show,
From each angry word and blow,
And from joy at others' woe,
　Keep us, Holy JESU.

From refusing to obey,
From forgetfulness to pray,
Lest we from Thy fold should stray,
　Keep us, Holy JESU.

That Thy Presence we may win,
From all thoughts and deeds of sin,—
All that is not pure within,—
　Keep us, Holy JESU.

III.

By Thy coming here to dwell,
God with us, EMMANUEL,
Saving us from sin and hell,
　Save us, Holy JESU.

By Thy Childhood's early years,
By Thy Infant griefs and fears,
By Thy sorrows and Thy tears,
　Save us, Holy JESU.

By Thy Blood for us outpoured,
By Thy Name by all adored,
Save us, JESU, God and LORD,
　Save us, Holy JESU.

V. HUTTON

156 Litany of Penitence.

LITANY A.
Unison.   11.10.11.7.   H. A. BRANSCOMBE.

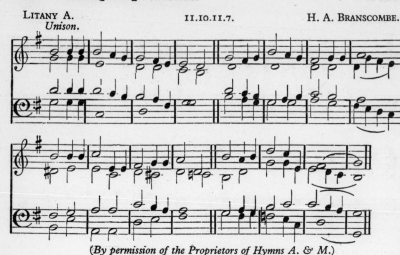

(By permission of the Proprietors of Hymns A. & M.)

FATHER, Whose love we have wronged by transgression,
CHRIST, Who wast nailed for our sins on the Tree,
SPIRIT, Who givest the grace of repentance;
    Hear us, we pray Thee, good LORD.

I.

JESU, adorable SAVIOUR of sinners,
Author of penitence, Hope of our souls,
Plentiful Fountain of grace and compassion:
    Hear us, we pray Thee, good LORD.

Thou Who didst empty Thyself of Thy
    glory,
Thou Who Thy parents on earth didst obey,
Thou Who for our sake enduredst temptation,
    Hear us, we pray Thee, good LORD.

Thou Who hast shown us the love of the
    FATHER,
Meeting with mercy the prodigal son,
Sonship and home to the lost one restoring,
    Hear us, we pray Thee, good LORD.

JESU, Who once by the well to the sinner
Clearly the sins of her heart didst reveal,
Leading her gently to faith and repentance,
    Hear us, we pray Thee, good LORD.

Thou Who didst enter the house of Zaccheus,
Blessing his faith and accepting his love,
When for wrong-doing he made restitution;
    Hear us, we pray Thee, good LORD.

II.

CHRIST, with the Twelve the last Passover
    keeping,   [slain,
Ere on the Cross the true LAMB should be
Sacrifice offered for all and for ever,
    Hear us, we pray Thee, good LORD.

JESU, alone with the blood-sweat upon Thee,
JESU, in agony bowed to the earth,
JESU, Thy will to the FATHER resigning;
    Hear us, we pray Thee, good LORD.

JESU, from Annas to Caiaphas hurried,
Blindfolded, stricken, and falsely accused,
Rudely blasphemed, and declared a blas-
    phemer;
    Hear us, we pray Thee, good LORD.

JESU, denied by Thine eager Apostle,
Whom with a look Thou didst straightway
    recall,
Moving him straightway to tears and contrition;
    Hear us, we pray Thee, good LORD.

Thou Who wast wounded to heal our trans-
    gressions,
Lifted on high to draw all men to Thee,
There on the Cross in Thy majesty reigning,
    Hear us, we pray Thee, good LORD.

The following should be sung at the end of either Part:

That Thou wouldst draw us to heart-felt contrition,
That Thou wouldst help us our sins to confess,
That Thou wouldst grant us the grace of amendment,
    Hear us, we pray Thee, good LORD.

That we may bring forth works meet for repentance,
That we give place to the devil no more,
That Thou wouldst lead us to sure perseverance,
    Hear us, we pray Thee, good LORD.

                                V. S. S. COLES, 1916.

157 Litany of Intercession.

St. Mark.
Unison.

7.7.7.6.

M. F. Bell.

Spare us, Ho - ly Tri - ni - ty.

(From the English Hymnal, by permission of the Oxford University Press.)

God the FATHER, God the SON,
God the SPIRIT, THREE in ONE,
Hear us from Thy heav'nly Throne,
    Spare us, Holy TRINITY.

JESU, evermore adored,
As we claim Thy promised word,
Gather'd in Thy Name, O LORD,
    Hear us, we beseech Thee.

For Thy Church so dear to Thee,
That she may for ever be
Kept in peace and unity,
    We beseech Thee, JESU.

For the rulers of our land,
That they may at Thy command
Right promote and wrong withstand,
    We beseech Thee, JESU.

For Thy priests in every place,
That relying on Thy Grace
They with patience run their race,
    We beseech Thee, JESU.

All our loved ones we commend,
LORD, to Thee, man's truest Friend,
Guard and guide them to the end,
    We beseech Thee, JESU.

Some on beds of sickness lie,
Some in want and hunger cry;
LORD, their every need supply,
    We beseech Thee, JESU.

Some are lonely, some are sad,
Some have lost the joy they had;
With true comfort make them glad,
    We beseech Thee, JESU.

Some have fallen from Thy Grace,
Wearied in their heav'nward race
May they rise and seek Thy Face
    We beseech Thee, JESU

Some are sunk in deadly sin
With no spark of love within ;
In their souls Thy work begin,
    We beseech Thee, JESU.

That whoever now doth lie
In his mortal agony
To the last may feel Thee nigh,
    We beseech Thee, JESU.

That the souls for whom we pray
Of the faithful pass'd away
May find mercy in that Day,
    We beseech Thee, JESU.

        V. HUTTON AND OTHERS.

POPLAR.

Bp. T. B. STRONG, 1908.

GOD be in my head, And in my un - der - stand - ing;

GOD be in my eyes, And in my look - - ing;

GOD be in my mouth, And in my speak - - ing;

GOD be in my heart, And in my think - - ing;

dim. e rall.

GOD be at my end, And . . . . . at my de - part - - - - - ing.

(From the Oxford Hymn Book.)

SARUM PRIMER, 1558.

159

Unison.

ANON.

God made— me to know and love and serve Him here on

earth, and to be— with Him for— ever - more in Heaven.

160 A Rule of Life (for Children).

Unison.

G. W. H.

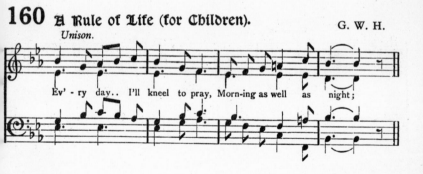

Ev'- ry day.. I'll kneel to pray, Morn-ing as well as night;

Ev'- ry week God's Altar I'll seek, And wor-ship in.. His sight...

W. H. F.

161 Act of Faith, Hope, and Love (for Children).

ANON.

1. O my God, I be-lieve in.. Thee; keep me ... safe.
2. O my God, I.. hope in.. Thee; keep me ... safe.
3. O my God, I.. do love Thee; keep me ... safe.

162 Act of Contrition (for Children).

G. W. H.

Je-sus suf-fered, Je-sus died! Oh, the cru-el shame!

Him they mocked and cru-ci-fied. I'm the one to blame.

E. F. N.

163 A Prayer of St. Richard of Chichester.

G. W. H.

O Ho-ly Je-sus, most mer-ci-ful Re-deem-er,

Friend and Bro - ther, May I know Thee more clear - ly, love Thee more dear - ly, and fol - low Thee more near - ly.

164

(I.)

Benedictus.

Blessed is He That cometh in the Name of the LORD. Hosanna in the highest.

(II.)

Agnus Dei.

O Lamb of GOD, That takest away the sins of the world, have mercy upon us.

O Lamb of GOD, That takest away the sins of the world, have mercy upon us.

O Lamb of GOD, That takest away the sins of the world, grant us Thy peace.

(III.) .

Agnus Dei.

O Lamb of GOD, That takest away the sins of the world, grant them rest.

O Lamb of GOD, That takest away the sins of the world, grant them rest.

O Lamb of GOD, That takest away the sins of the world, grant them rest everlasting.

165 (I)

VERBUM SUPERNUM PRODIENS.

Harmonised by J. H. A.

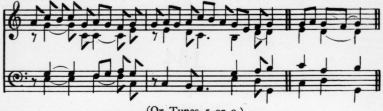

A - men.

(Or Tunes 5 or 9.)

O SAVING Victim ! opening wide
    The gate of Heaven to man below ;
Our foes press hard on every side ;
    Thine aid supply, Thy strength bestow.

All praise and thanks to Thee ascend
    For evermore, blest ONE in THREE ;
O grant us life that shall not end
    In our true native land with Thee.

165 (II)

ST. AUDREY.
   (*First Tune.*)
      Slow and Majestic. Unison.

8.7.8.7.8.7.

BASIL HARWOOD.

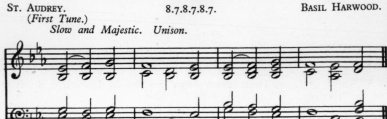

The Pedal part well marked

II.

Tantum ergo.

THEREFORE we, before Him bending,
    This great Sacrament revere ;
Types and shadows have their ending,
    For the newer rite is here ;
Faith, our outward sense befriending,
    Makes the inward vision clear.

Glory let us give, and blessing
    To the FATHER, and the SON ;
Honour, might, and praise addressing,
    While eternal ages run ;
Ever, too, His love confessing,
    Who, from Both, with Both is One.

TANTUM ERGO.
(*Second Tune.*)

8.7.8.7.8.7

ANON.

II.

Tantum ergo.

THEREFORE we, before Him bending,
   This great Sacrament revere ;
Types and shadows have their ending,
   For the newer rite is here ;
Faith, our outward sense befriending,
   Makes the inward vision clear.

Glory let us give, and blessing
   To the FATHER, and the SON ;
Honour, might, and praise addressing,
   While eternal ages run ;
Ever, too, His love confessing,
   Who, from Both, with Both is One.

165(II)

8.7.8.7.8.7.

(*Third Tune.*) *Unison.*

A. E. TOZER.

Harmony.

Org.

(*By permission of Cary & Co., 13 & 15, Mortimer Street, London, W.1.*)

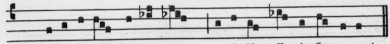

Ant. Let us a - dore CHRIST, our LORD : in the Most Ho - ly Sac - ra - ment

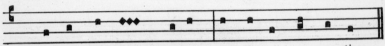

Ps. 117 O praise the LORD, all ye peo-ple : praise Him all ye na - tions.

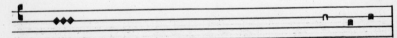

For His merciful kindness is ever more and more to - wards us

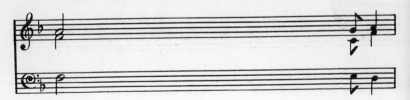

And the truth of the LORD endureth for ev-er, Praise the LORD

Glory be... the SON : and to the HO-LY GHOST,

As it was... shall be :world with-out end. A-men.

Repeat Antiphon.

III.

PSALM 117.

ANTIPHON. Let us adore CHRIST, our LORD : in the Most Holy Sacrament.

1. O praise the LORD, all ye people : praise Him all ye nations.

2. For His merciful kindness is ever more and more towards us : and the truth of the LORD endureth for ever. Praise the LORD.

Glory be to the FATHER, and to the SON : and to the HOLY GHOST;

As it was in the beginning, is now, and ever shall be : world without end. Amen.

ANT. Let us adore CHRIST, our LORD : in the Most Holy Sacrament.

IV.

THE DIVINE PRAISES.

Blessed be GOD.
Blessed be His Holy Name.
Blessed be JESUS CHRIST, true GOD and true man.
Blessed be the Name of JESUS.
Blessed be JESUS CHRIST in the most holy sacrament
of the Altar.
Blessed be the HOLY GHOST, the Comforter.
Blessed be the Great Mother of GOD, Mary most holy.
Blessed be the Name of Mary, Virgin and Mother.
Blessed be God in His Angels and His Saints.

166

O SAVIOUR of the world, Who by Thy Cross and precious Blood hast redeemed us, save us and help us, we humbly beseech Thee, O LORD.

II.

℣. We adore Thee, O CHRIST, and we bless Thee :
℟. *Because by Thy Holy Cross Thou hast redeemed the world.*

FROM PAIN TO PAIN, FROM
WOE TO WOE.

G. W. HART, C.R., 1925.

Not too fast.

From pain to pain, from woe to woe, with lov-ing hearts and

foot - steps slow, To Cal - va - ry with Christ we go.

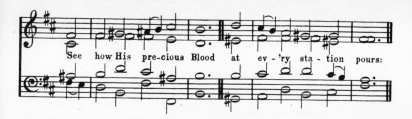

See how His pre-cious Blood at ev-'ry sta-tion pours:

Was ev-er grief like His:— Was ev-er sin like ours.

167

Anima Christi.

Soul of CHRIST, sanctify me.
Body of CHRIST, save me.
Blood of CHRIST, refresh me.
Water from the Side of CHRIST, wash me.
Passion of CHRIST, strengthen me.
O Good JESU, hear me.
Within Thy Wounds hide me.
Suffer me not to be separated from Thee.
From the malicious enemy defend me.
In the hour of my death call me,
And bid me come to Thee.
That with Thy Saints I may praise Thee
For ever and ever.   Amen.

168

An Act of Faith.

My God, I believe in Thee, and all Thy Church doth teach, because Thou hast said it, and Thy word is true.

An Act of Hope.

My God, I hope in Thee, for grace and for glory, because of Thy promises, Thy mercy and Thy power.

An Act of Love.

My God, I love Thee with all my heart, because Thou art so good; and for Thy sake I love my neighbour as myself.

An Act of Contrition.

O my God, I am very sorry for all the sins by which I have offended Thee, and I resolve to try by Thy Grace never to sin again.

An Act of Consecration.

O my God, I give myself to Thee, in union with the offering of Jesus Christ on the Holy Cross.

169

Psalm 51.

Have mercy upon me, O God, after Thy great goodness : according to the multitude of Thy mercies do away mine offences.

2. Wash me throughly from my wickedness : and cleanse me from my sin.

3. For I acknowledge my faults : and my sin is ever before me.

4. Against Thee only have I sinned, and done this evil in Thy sight : that Thou mightest be justified in Thy saying, and clear when Thou art judged.

5. Behold, I was shapen in wickedness : and in sin hath my mother conceived me.

6. But lo, Thou requirest truth in the inward parts: and shalt make me to understand wisdom secretly.

7. Thou shalt purge me with hyssop, and I shall be clean : Thou shalt wash me, and I shall be whiter than snow.

8. Thou shalt make me hear of joy and gladness : that the bones which Thou hast broken may rejoice.

9. Turn Thy Face from my sins : and put out all my misdeeds.

10. Make me a clean heart, O God : and renew a right spirit within me.

11. Cast me not away from Thy Presence : and take not Thy Holy Spirit from me.

12. O give me the comfort of Thy help again :
and stablish me with Thy free Spirit.

13. Then shall I teach Thy ways unto the wicked :
and sinners shall be converted unto Thee.

14. Deliver me from blood-guiltiness, O GOD,
Thou that art the GOD of my health : and my tongue
shall sing of Thy righteousness.

15. Thou shalt open my lips, O LORD : and my
mouth shall show Thy praise.

16. For Thou desirest no sacrifice, else would I
give it Thee : but Thou delightest not in burnt-
offerings.

17. The sacrifice of GOD is a troubled spirit : a
broken and contrite heart, O GOD, shalt Thou
not despise.

18. O be favourable and gracious unto Sion :
build Thou the walls of Jerusalem.

19. Then shalt Thou be pleased with the sacrifice
of righteousness, with the burnt-offerings and
oblations : then shall they offer young bullocks
upon Thine Altar.

Glory be to the FATHER, and to the SON : and to
the HOLY GHOST ;

As it was in the beginning, is now, and ever shall
be : world without end.   Amen.

170

PSALM 130.

OUT of the deep have I called unto Thee, O LORD :
LORD, hear my voice.

2. O let Thine ears consider well : the voice of
my complaint.

3. If Thou, LORD, wilt be extreme to mark what
is done amiss : O LORD, who may abide it ?

4. For there is mercy with Thee : therefore shalt
Thou be feared.

5. I look for the LORD ; my soul doth wait for
Him : in His Word is my trust.

6. My soul fleeth unto the LORD : before the
morning watch, I say, before the morning watch.

7. O Israel, trust in the LORD, for with the LORD
there is mercy : and with Him is plenteous redemption.

8. And He shall redeem Israel : from all his sins.

Glory be to the FATHER, and to the SON : and to
the HOLY GHOST ;

As it was in the beginning, is now, and ever shall
be : world without end.   Amen.

171

PSALM 103.

PRAISE the LORD, O my soul : and all that is
within me praise His holy Name.

2. Praise the LORD, O my soul : and forget not
all His benefits ;

3. Who forgiveth all thy sin : and healeth all
thine infirmities ;

4. Who saveth thy life from destruction : and
crowneth thee with mercy and lovingkindness ;

5. Who satisfieth thy mouth with good things : making thee young and lusty as an eagle.

6. The LORD executeth righteousness and judgement : for all them that are oppressed with wrong.

7. He showeth His ways unto Moses : His works unto the children of Israel.

8. The LORD is full of compassion and mercy : long-suffering, and of great goodness.

9. He will not alway be chiding : neither keepeth He His anger for ever.

10. He hath not dealt with us after our sins : nor rewarded us according to our wickednesses.

11. For look how high the heaven is in comparison of the earth : so great is His mercy also toward them that fear Him.

12. Look how wide also the east is from the west : so far hath He set our sins from us.

13. Yea, like as a father pitieth his own children : even so is the LORD merciful unto them that fear Him.

14. For He knoweth whereof we are made : He remembereth that we are but dust.

15. The days of man are but as grass : for he flourisheth as a flower of the field.

16. For as soon as the wind goeth over it, it is gone : and the place thereof shall know it no more.

17. But the merciful goodness of the LORD endureth for ever and ever upon them that fear Him : and His righteousness upon children's children ;

18. Even upon such as keep His covenant : and think upon His commandments to do them.

19.. The LORD hath prepared His seat in Heaven : and His Kingdom ruleth over all.

20. O praise the LORD, ye angels of His, ye that excel in strength : ye that fulfil His commandment, and hearken unto the Voice of His words.

21. O praise the LORD, all ye His hosts : ye servants of His that do His pleasure.

22. O speak good of the LORD, all ye works of His, in all places of His dominion : praise thou the LORD, O my soul.

Glory be to the FATHER, and to the SON : and to the HOLY GHOST ;

As it was in the beginning, is now, and ever shall be, world without end.   Amen.

172

PSALM 150.

O PRAISE God in His holiness : praise Him in the firmament of His power.

2. Praise Him in His noble acts : praise Him according to His excellent greatness.

3. Praise Him in the sound of the trumpet : praise Him upon the lute and harp.

4. Praise Him in the cymbals and dances : praise Him upon the strings and pipe.

5. Praise Him upon the well-tuned cymbals : praise Him upon the loud cymbals.

6. Let every thing that hath breath : praise the LORD.

Glory be to the FATHER, and to the SON : and to the HOLY GHOST ;

As it was in the beginning, is now, and ever shall be : world without end.   Amen.

173

Te Deum.

WE praise Thee, O GOD : we acknowledge Thee to be the LORD.

All the earth doth worship Thee : the FATHER everlasting.

To Thee all Angels cry aloud : the Heavens and all the Powers therein.

To Thee Cherubim and Seraphim : continually do cry.

Holy, Holy, Holy : LORD GOD of Sabaoth ;

Heaven and earth are full of the Majesty : of Thy glory.

The glorious company of the Apostles : praise Thee.

The goodly fellowship of the Prophets : praise Thee.

The noble army of Martyrs · praise Thee.

The holy Church throughout all the world : doth acknowledge Thee ;

The FATHER : of an infinite Majesty ;

Thine honourable, true : and only SON ;

Also the HOLY GHOST : the Comforter.

Thou art the King of Glory : O CHRIST.

Thou art the everlasting SON : of the FATHER.

When Thou tookest upon Thee to deliver man : Thou didst not abhor the Virgin's womb.

When Thou hadst overcome the sharpness of death : Thou didst open the Kingdom of Heaven to all believers.

Thou sittest at the right hand of GOD : in the glory of the FATHER.

We believe that Thou shalt come : to be our Judge.

We therefore pray Thee, help Thy servants : whom Thou hast redeemed with Thy precious Blood.

Make them to be numbered with Thy Saints : in glory everlasting.

O LORD, save Thy people : and bless Thine heritage.

Govern them : and lift them up for ever.

Day by day : we magnify Thee ;

And we worship Thy Name : ever world without end.

Vouchsafe, O LORD : to keep us this day without sin.

O LORD, have mercy upon us : have mercy upon us.

O LORD, let Thy mercy lighten upon us : as our trust is in Thee.

O LORD, in Thee have I trusted : let me never be confounded.

174

Magnificat.

MY soul doth magnify the LORD : and my spirit hath rejoiced in GOD my SAVIOUR.

For He hath regarded : the lowliness of His hand-maiden.

For behold, from henceforth : all generations shall call me blessed.

For He that is mighty hath magnified me : and holy is His Name.

And His mercy is on them that fear Him : throughout all generations.

He hath showed strength with His arm : He hath scattered the proud in the imagination of their hearts.

He hath put down the mighty from their seat: and hath exalted the humble and meek.

He hath filled the hungry with good things : and the rich He hath sent empty away.

He remembering His mercy hath holpen His servant Israel : as He promised to our forefathers, Abraham and his seed, for ever.

Glory be to the FATHER, and to the SON : and to the HOLY GHOST ;

As it was in the beginning, is now, and ever shall be : world without end. Amen.

175

Nunc Dimittis.

LORD, now lettest Thou Thy servant depart in peace : according to Thy word.

For mine eyes hath seen : Thy salvation.

Which Thou hast prepared : before the face of all people ;

To be a Light to lighten the Gentiles : and to be the glory of Thy people Israel.

Glory be to the FATHER, and to the SON : and to the HOLY GHOST ;

As it was in the beginning, is now, and ever shall be : world without end. Amen.

176

ADVENT tells us, CHRIST is near :
Christmas tells us CHRIST is here !
In Epiphany we trace
All the glory of His grace.

Those three Sundays before Lent
Will prepare us to repent ;
That in Lent we may begin
Earnestly to mourn for sin.

Holy Week and Easter, then,
Tell Who died and rose again :
O that happy Easter Day !
" CHRIST is risen indeed," we say.

Yes, and CHRIST ascended, too,
To prepare a place for you ;
So we give Him special praise,
After those great Forty Days.

Then He sent the HOLY GHOST,
On the Day of Pentecost,
With us ever to abide ;
Well may we keep Whitsuntide !

Last of all, we humbly sing
Glory to our GOD and KING,
Glory to the ONE IN THREE,
On the Feast of Trinity.

K. HANKEY, 1834-1911

DIX.

7·7·7·7·7·7.   *Abridged from a Chorale, " Treue Heiland," by* C. KOCHER, 1786-1872.

As with gladness men of old
Did the guiding star behold,
As with joy they hailed its light,
Leading onward, beaming bright,
So, most gracious GOD, may we
Evermore be led to Thee.

As with joyful steps they sped,
To that lowly manger-bed,
There to bend the knee before
Him Whom heaven and earth adore.
So may we with willing feet
Ever seek Thy mercy-seat.

As they offered gifts most rare
At that manger rude and bare,
So may we with holy joy,
Pure, and free from sin's alloy,
All our costliest treasures bring,
CHRIST, to Thee our heavenly King.

Holy JESU, every day
Keep us in the narrow way ;
And, when earthly things are past,
Bring our ransomed souls at last
Where they need no star to guide,
Where no clouds Thy glory hide.

In the heavenly country bright
Need they no created light ;
Thou its Light, its Joy, its Crown,
Thou its Sun which goes not down :
There for ever may we sing
Alleluyas to our King.

W. CHATTERTON DIX, 1860.

178

CRANHAM.   6.5.6.5.D.   G. VON HOLST.

Cast thy care on JESUS,
  Make Him now thy Friend,
Tell Him all thy troubles,
  Trust Him to the end ;
He is Man and Brother,
  He is LORD and GOD,
And the way of sorrows
  Is the path He trod.

Cast thy care on JESUS,
  Nothing is too small
For His vast compassion ;
  He can feel for all ;
In the gloom and darkness
  Clasp His living Hand,
He will guide and cheer thee
  Through the desert land.

Cast thy care on JESUS
  Tell Him all thy sin,
All thy fierce temptations
  And the wrong within ;
He Himself was tempted,
  And He pleads above
For the soul that asketh
  Pardon through His love.

Cast thy care on JESUS ;
  What is death to those
Who in deep submission
  On His love repose,
But a short step further,
  Nearer to His side,
When thine eyes shall see Him
  And be satisfied.

F. G. SCOTT, 1861.

179

8.7.8.7.8.7. *Melody from S. WEBBE'S*
" Motetts or Antiphons," 1792.

CHRIST, enthroned in highest heaven,
  Hear us crying from the deep,
For the faithful ones departed,
  For the souls of all that sleep ;
As Thy kneeling Church entreateth,
  Hearken, Shepherd of the sheep.

King of Glory, hear our voices,
  Grant Thy faithful rest, we pray ;
We have sinned, and may not bide it,
  If Thou mark our steps astray,
Yet we plead that saving Victim,
  Which for them we bring to-day.

That which Thou Thyself hast offered
  To Thy Father, offer we ;
Let it win for them a blessing,
  Bless them, JESU, set them free :
They are Thine, they wait in patience,
  Merciful and gracious be.

They are Thine, O take them quickly,
  Thou their Hope, O raise them high ;
Ever hoping, ever trusting,
  Unto Thee they strive and cry ;
Day and night, both morn and even,
  Be, O Christ, their Guardian nigh.

Let Thy plenteous loving-kindness
  On them, as we pray, be poured ;
Let them through Thy boundless mercy,
  From all evil be restored ;
Hearken to the gentle pleading
  Of Thy Mother, gracious LORD.

When, O kind and radiant JESU,
  Kneels the Queen Thy throne before,
Let the court of Saints attending,
  Mercy for the dead implore ;
Hearken, loving Friend of sinners,
  Whom the Cross exalted bore.

Hear and answer prayers devoutest,
  Break, O LORD, each binding chain,
Dash the gates of death asunder,
  Quell the devil and his train ;
Bring the souls which Thou hast ransomed
  Evermore in joy to reign.

13th Cent. *Tr.* R. F. LITTLEDALE.

180

COELITES PLAUDANT.   11.11.11.5.   *Rouen Church Melody.*

In Unison.

A - men.

(From the English Hymnal, by permission of the Oxford University Press.)

CHRIST, the fair glory of the holy Angels,
Thou Who hast made us, Thou Who o'er us rulest,
Grant of Thy mercy unto us Thy servants
    Steps up to heaven.

Send Thy Archangel, Michael, to our succour;
Peacemaker blessèd, may he banish from us
Striving and hatred, so that for the peaceful
    All things may prosper.

Send Thy Archangel, Gabriel, the mighty;
Herald of heaven, may he from us mortals
Spurn the old serpent, watching o'er the temples
    Where Thou art worshipped.

Send. Thy Archangel, Raphael, the restorer
Of the misguided ways of men who wander,
Who at Thy bidding strengthens soul and body
    With Thine anointing.

May the blest Mother of our GOD and SAVIOUR,
May the assembly of the Saints in glory,
May the celestial companies of Angels
    Ever assist us.

FATHER Almighty, SON and HOLY SPIRIT,
GOD ever blessèd, be Thou our preserver;
Thine is the glory which the Angels worship,
    Veiling their faces. Amen.

9th Cent., Tr. A. R. & P. D.

181

C.M. *Adapted from* T. HAWEIS, 1734-1820,
by S. WEBBE (the younger).

(A lower setting will be found at No. 132.)

CITY of GOD, how broad and far
  Outspread thy walls sublime !
The true thy chartered freemen are
  Of every age and clime.

One holy Church, one army strong,
  One steadfast, high intent ;
One working band, one harvest-song,
  One King omnipotent.

How purely hath thy speech come down
  From man's primaeval youth !
How grandly hath thine empire grown
  Of freedom, love and truth !

How gleam thy watch-fires through the night,
  With never-fainting ray !
How rise thy towers, serene and bright,
  To meet the dawning day !

In vain the surge's angry shock,
  In vain the drifting sands :
Unharmed upon the eternal Rock
  The eternal City stands.

S. JOHNSON, 1822-82.

182

DOWN AMPNEY.   6.6.11.D.   R. VAUGHAN WILLIAMS.

(From the English Hymnal, by permission of the Oxford University Press.

COME down, O Love divine,
Seek Thou this soul of mine,
And visit it with Thine own ardour glowing;
O Comforter, draw near,
Within my heart appear,
And kindle it, Thy holy flame bestowing.

O let it freely burn,
Till earthly passions turn
To dust and ashes in its heat consuming;
And let Thy glorious light
Shine ever on my sight,
And clothe me round, the while my path illuming.

Let holy charity
Mine outward vesture be,
And lowliness become mine inner clothing;
True lowliness of heart,
Which takes the humbler part,
And o'er its own shortcomings weeps with loathing.

And so the yearning strong,
With which the soul will long,
Shall far outpass the power of human telling;
For none can guess its grace,
Till he become the place
Wherein the Holy Spirit makes His dwelling.

BIANCO of SIENA, 1434.
Tr. R. F. LITTLEDALE.

183

ST. ANDREW   8.7.8.7.   E. H. THORNE, 1875.

(By permission of the Proprietors of Hymns A. & M.)

COME, Thou long-expected JESUS,
   Born to set Thy people free ;
From our fears and sins release us ;
   Let us find our rest in Thee.

Israel's strength and consolation,
   Hope of all the earth Thou art ;
Dear Desire of every nation,
   Joy of every longing heart.

Born Thy people to deliver ;
   Born a Child and yet a King ;
Born to reign in us for ever ;
   Now Thy gracious kingdom bring.

By Thy own eternal Spirit,
   Rule in all our hearts alone ;
By Thy all-sufficient merit,
   Raise us to Thy glorious throne.

                           C. WESLEY, 1744.

184

ETERNAL FATHER, strong to save,
Whose Arm doth bind the restless wave,
Who bidd'st the mighty ocean deep
Its own appointed limits keep :
   O hear us when we cry to Thee
   For those in peril on the sea.

O SAVIOUR, Whose almighty word
The winds and waves submissive heard,
Who walkedst on the foaming deep,
And calm amid its rage didst sleep :
   O hear us when we cry to Thee
   For those in peril on the sea.

O Sacred Spirit, Who didst brood,
Upon the chaos dark and rude,
Who bad'st its angry tumult cease,
And gavest light and life and peace :
   O hear us when we cry to Thee
   For those in peril on the sea.

O Trinity of love and power,
Our brethren shield in danger's hour ;
From rock and tempest, fire and foe,
Protect them wheresoe'er they go :
   And ever let there rise to Thee
   Glad hymns of praise from land and sea.

               W. WHITING, 1825-78.

185

8.8.7.8.8.7.D.

Composed or adapted by
M. GREITER, *c.* 1525.

FAITH of our Fathers, taught of old
By faithful shepherds of the fold,
    The hallowing of our nation;
Thou wast through many a wealthy year,
Through many a darkened day of fear,
    The rock of our salvation.
Arise, arise, good Christian men,
Your glorious standard raise again,
    The Cross of CHRIST Who calls you,
Who bids you live and bids you die
For His great cause, and stands on high
    To witness what befalls you.

Our fathers heard the trumpet call
Through lowly cot and kingly hall
    From oversea resounding;
They bowed their stubborn wills to learn
The truths that live, the thoughts that burn,
    With new resolve abounding.
Arise, arise, good Christian men,
Your glorious standard raise again,
    The Cross of CHRIST Who guides you,
Whose Arm is bared to join the fray,
Who marshals you in stern array,
    Fearless, whate'er betides you.

Our fathers held the faith received,
By saints declared, by saints believed,
    By saints in death defended;
Through pain of doubt and bitterness,
Through pain of treason and distress,
    They for the right contended.
Arise, arise, good Christian men,
Your glorious standard raise again,
    The Cross of CHRIST Who bought you,
Who leads you forth in this new age
With long-enduring hearts to wage
    The warfare He has taught you.

Though frequent be the loud alarms,
Though still we march by ambushed arms
    Of death and hell surrounded,
With CHRIST for Chief we fear no foe,
Nor force nor craft can overthrow
    The Church that He has founded.
Arise, arise, good Christian men,
Your glorious standard raise again,
    The Cross wherewith He signed you,
The King Himself shall lead you on,
Shall watch you till the strife be done,
    Then near His throne shall find you.

                        T. A. LACEY.

186

SINE NOMINE.   10.10.10.4.   R. VAUGHAN WILLIAMS.

In moderate time.

Unison.

(*From the English Hymnal, by permission of the Oxford University Press.*)

For all the saints who from their labours rest,
Who | Thee by | faith before the world confessed,
Thy | name, O | Jesu, be for ever blest.   Alleluia !

Thou wast their Rock, their Fortress, and their Might;
| Thou, Lord, their | Captain in the well-fought
fight ;
| Thou in the | darkness drear their one true Light.
Alleluia !

O, may Thy soldiers, faithful, true, and bold,
Fight as the | Saints who nobly fought of old,
And | win, with | them, the victor's crown of gold.
Alleluia !

O blest communion ! fellowship divine !
We feebly | struggle ; they in glory shine !
Yet | all are | one in Thee, for all are Thine.
Alleluia !

And when the strife is fierce, the warfare long,
| Steals on the | ear the distant triumph-song,
And | hearts are | brave a- | gain, and arms are
strong.   Alleluia !

The golden evening brightens in the west :
Soon, soon, to | faithful warriors cometh rest ;
Sweet is the | calm of Paradise the blest.   Alleluia !

But lo, there breaks a yet more glorious day !
The | Saints tri- | umphant rise in bright array ;
The | King of | glory | passes on His way.   Alleluia !

From earth's wide bounds, from ocean's farthest
coast,
Through | gates of | pearl streams in the countless
. host,
| Singing to | Father, Son, and Holy Ghost.
Alleluia !

W. Walsham How, 1823-97.

225

187

BUNESSAN.   IRREGULAR.   *Old Gaelic Melody.*

(From " Songs of Praise," by permission of the Oxford University Press.)

GLORY to JESUS,
Glory to JESUS,
Glory to JESUS,
    JESUS our GOD.
Praise Him for living,
Praise Him for dying,
Praise Him for giving
    His Body and Blood.

Sinners around Thee
Mocked Thee and bound Thee,
Wounded and crowned Thee,
    Their bitter loss.
Hark to our crying,
On Thee relying,
JESUS our dying
    King on the Cross.

Child of the Manger,
Tenderest Stranger,
We are in danger,
    Sorrow and sin.
Shepherds adore Thee,
Kings bow before Thee,
LORD, we implore Thee,
    Thy work begin.

LORD, Thou hast spoken,
And by that token,
Where bread is broken,
    Wine is outpoured,
There we extol Thee,
Worshippers lowly,
In Thy most Holy
    Sacrament, LORD.

Be Thou beside us,
Whate'er betide us,
Only Thou guide us,
    And set us free.
When we have striven,
JESUS, in heaven,
Ransom'd, forgiven,
    Call us to Thee.

V. SHEARBURN, C.R., 1933.

188

CAERSALEM. 8.7.8.7.4.7. *Welsh Hymn Melody*

GUIDE me, O Thou great Redeemer,
  Pilgrim through this barren land ;
I am weak, but Thou art mighty,
  Hold me with Thy powerful Hand :
    Bread of heaven,
Feed me till I want no more.

Open now the crystal fountain,
  Whence the healing stream doth flow ;
Let the fire and cloudy pillar
  Lead me all my journey through :
    Strong Deliverer,
Be Thou still my strength and shield.

When I tread the verge of Jordan,
  Bid my anxious fears subside ;
Death of death, and hell's destruction,
  Land me safe on Canaan's side :
    Songs of praises
I will ever give to Thee.

W. WILLIAMS, 1717-91.

189

HAIL, O Star that pointest
   Towards the port of heaven,
Thou to whom as maiden
   GOD for SON was given.

When the salutation
   Gabriel had spoken,
Peace was shed upon us,
   Eden's bonds were broken.

Bound by Satan's fetters,
   Health and vision needing,
God will aid and light us
   At thy gentle pleading.

JESU's tender Mother,
   Make thy supplication
Unto Him Who chose thee
   At His Incarnation ;

That, O matchless Maiden,
   Passing meek and lowly,
Thy dear SON may make us
   Blameless, chaste and holy.

So, as now we journey,
   Aid our weak endeavour,
Till we gaze on JESUS,
   And rejoice for ever.

FATHER, SON and SPIRIT,
   THREE in ONE confessing,
Give we equal glory,
   Equal praise and blessing.

c. 9th Cent., Tr. A. RILEY.

190

A - men.

HE, whose confession GOD of old accepted,
Whom through the ages all now hold in honour,
Gaining his guerdon this day came to enter
　　Heaven's high portal.

God-fearing, watchful, pure of mind and body,
Holy and humble, thus did all men find him ;
While, through his members, to the life immortal
　　Mortal life called him.

Thus to the weary, from the life enshrinèd,
Potent in virtue, flowed humane compassion ;
Sick and sore laden, howsoever burdened,
　　There they found healing.

So now in chorus, giving GOD the glory,
Raise we our anthem gladly to his honour,
That in fair kinship we may all be sharers
　　Here and hereafter.

Honour and glory, power and salvation,
Be in the highest unto Him Who reigneth
Changeless in heaven over earthly changes,
　　Triune, eternal. Amen.

　　　　　　　　　8th Cent. *Tr.* L. H.

191

St. Denio.　　　　II.II.II.II.　　　　*Welsh Hymn Melody.*

In moderate time.

IMMORTAL, invisible, GOD only wise,
In light inaccessible hid from our eyes,
Most blessèd, most glorious, the Ancient of Days,
Almighty, victorious, Thy great name we praise.

Unresting, unhasting, and silent as light,
Nor wanting, nor wasting, Thou rulest in might ;
Thy justice like mountains high soaring above
Thy clouds which are fountains of goodness and love

To all life Thou givest—to both great and small ;
In all life Thou livest, the true life of all ;
We blossom and flourish as leaves on the tree,
And wither and perish—but nought changeth Thee

Great Father of Glory, pure Father of Light,
Thine angels adore Thee, all veiling their sight ;
All laud we would render : O help us to see
'Tis only the splendour of light hideth Thee.

W. CHALMERS SMITH, 1824-1908.

192

JESUS Divine,
Sweet Brother mine,
 Be with me all the day,

And when the light
Has turned to night,
 Be with me still, I pray.

Where'er I be,
Come Thou with me,
 And never go away.

    FR. ROCHE, S.J.

(From "A Child's Prayers to Jesus," by permission of Longmans, Green & Co. Ltd.)

193

Jesu, good above all other,
Gentle Child of gentle Mother,
In a stable born our Brother,
　Give us grace to persevere.

Jesu, cradled in a manger,
For us facing every danger,
Living as a homeless stranger,
　Make we Thee our King most dear.

Jesu, for Thy people dying,
Risen Master, death defying,
Lord in heaven, Thy grace supplying,
　Keep us by Thine Altar near.

Jesu, Who our sorrows bearest,
All our thoughts and hopes Thou sharest,
Thou to man the truth declarest ;
　Help us all Thy truth to hear.

Lord, in all our doings guide us ;
Pride and hate shall ne'er divide us ;
We'll go on with Thee beside us,
　And with joy we'll persevere !

P. D.

194

TRURO.　　　　　　　L.M.　　　　*Psalmodia Evangelica*, 1790.

JESUS shall reign where'er the sun
Does his successive journeys run ;
His kingdom stretch from shore to shore,
Till moons shall wax and wane no more.

People and realms of every tongue
Dwell on His love with sweetest song ;
And infant voices shall proclaim
Their early blessings on His name.

Blessings abound where'er He reigns ;
The prisoner leaps to lose his chains ;
The weary find eternal rest,
And all the sons of want are blest.

Let every creature rise and bring
Peculiar honours to our King ;
Angels descend with songs again,
And earth repeat the long amen.

I. WATTS, 1674-1748.

233

195

Jesus, these eyes have never seen
    That radiant form of Thine ;
The veil of sense hangs dark between
    Thy blessèd Face and mine.

I see Thee not, I hear Thee not,
    Yet art Thou oft with me ;
And earth hath ne'er so dear a spot
    As where I met with Thee.

Yet, though I have not seen, and still
    Must rest in faith alone,
I love Thee, dearest Lord, and will,
    Unseen, but not unknown.

When death these mortal eyes shall seal,
    And still this throbbing heart,
The rending veil shall Thee reveal
    All glorious as Thou art.

                                   Ray Palmer, 1808–1887.

196

REX GLORIOSE MARTYRUM.   L.M.   *Catholische Geistliche Gesange*, 1608.

(Or Tune 211.)

Lo! round the throne, a glorious band,
The Saints in countless myriads stand,
Of every tongue redeem'd to GOD,
Array'd in garments wash'd in Blood.

Through tribulation great they came;
They bore the cross, despised the shame;
From all their labours now they rest,
In GOD's eternal glory blest.

They see their Saviour face to face,
And sing the triumphs of His grace;
Him day and night they ceaseless praise,
To Him the loud thanksgiving raise:

" Worthy the LAMB, for sinners slain,
Through endless years to live and reign;
Thou hast redeem'd us by Thy Blood,
And made us kings and priests to GOD."

O may we tread the sacred road
That Saints and holy Martyrs trod;
Wage to the end the glorious strife,
And win, like them, a crown of life.

R. HILL, 1783.

197

WESTMINSTER.   C.M.   J. TURLE, 1802-1882.

My God, how wonderful Thou art,
　　Thy majesty how bright,
How beautiful Thy mercy-seat,
　　In depths of burning light!

How dread are Thine eternal years,
　　O everlasting Lord.
By prostrate spirits day and night
　　Incessantly adored!

How wonderful, how beautiful,
　　The sight of Thee must be,
Thine endless wisdom, boundless power,
　　And awful purity!

O, how I fear Thee, living God,
　　With deepest, tenderest fears,
And worship Thee with trembling hope,
　　And penitential tears!

Yet I may love Thee, too, O Lord,
　　Almighty as Thou art,
For Thou hast stooped to ask of me
　　The love of my poor heart.

No earthly father loves like Thee,
　　No mother, e'er so mild,
Bears and forbears as Thou hast done
　　With me Thy sinful child.

Father of Jesus, love's reward,
　　What rapture will it be
Prostrate before Thy throne to lie,
　　And gaze and gaze on Thee.

F. W. Faber, 1814-1863.

198

ROTHWELL.
(First Tune.)
6.4.6.4.6.6.4.
GEOFFREY SHAW.

NEARER, my GOD, to Thee,
  Nearer to Thee;
E'en though it be a cross
  That raiseth me ;
Still all my song shall be,
" Nearer, my GOD, to Thee,
  Nearer to Thee."

Though, like the wanderer,
  The sun gone down,
Darkness comes over me,
  My rest a stone ;
Yet in my dreams I'd be
Nearer, my GOD, to Thee,
  Nearer to Thee.

There let my way appear
  Steps unto heaven,
All that Thou sendest me
  In mercy given,
Angels to beckon me
Nearer, my GOD, to Thee,
  Nearer to Thee.

Then, with my waking thoughts
  Bright with Thy praise,
Out of my stony griefs
  Beth-el I'll raise ;
So by my woes to be
Nearer, my GOD, to Thee,
  Nearer to Thee.

SARAH F. ADAMS, 1805-1848.

198

6.4.6.4.6.6.4.

J. B. DYKES, 1823-1876.

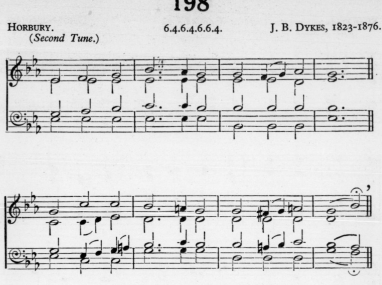

199

NUN DANKET.   6.7.6.7.6.6.6.6.   J. CRUGER, 1598-1662.

Very slow and majestic.

Now thank we all our GOD,
With heart and hands and voices,
  Who wondrous things hath done,
In Whom His world rejoices;
  Who from our mother's arms
    Hath blessed us on our way
With countless gifts of love,
    And still is ours to-day.

O may this bounteous GOD
Through all our life be near us,
  With ever joyful hearts
And blessèd peace to cheer us;
  And keep us in His grace,
    And guide us when perplexed,
And free us from all ills
    In this world and the next.

All praise and thanks to GOD
The FATHER now be given,
  The SON, and Him Who reigns
With them in highest heaven,
  The One eternal GOD,
    Whom earth and heaven adore;
For thus it was, is now,
    And shall be evermore.

M. RINKART, 1586-1649.
Tr. C. WINKWORTH.

239

LUCIS CREATOR.
In Unison.

L.M.

Angers Church Melody.

A - men.

O BLEST Creator of the light,
Who mak'st the day with radiance bright,
And o'er the forming world didst call
The light from chaos first of all ;

Whose wisdom joined in meet array
The morn and eve, and named them Day :
Night comes with all its darkling fears ;
Regard Thy people's prayers and tears,

Lest, sunk in sin, and whelm'd with strife,
They lose the gift of endless life ;
While thinking but the thoughts of time,
They weave new chains of woe and crime.

But grant them grace that they may strain
The heavenly gate and prize to gain ·
Each harmful lure aside to cast,
And purge away each error past.

O FATHER, that we ask be done,
Through JESUS CHRIST, Thine only SON ;
Who, with the HOLY GHOST and Thee,
Doth live and reign eternally.   Amen.

6th Cent. *Tr.* J. M. NEALE.

201

S. CATHERINE   7.6.7.6.D.   R. F. DALE.

(Or Tune 111.)

O JESU, Thou art standing
  Outside the fast-closed door,
In lowly patience waiting
  To pass the threshold o'er :
Shame on us, Christian brethren,
  His Name and sign who bear,
O shame, thrice shame upon us
  To keep Him standing there !

O JESU, Thou art knocking :
  And lo ! that Hand is scarr'd,
And thorns Thy Brow encircle,
  And tears Thy Face have marr'd :
O love that passeth knowledge
  So patiently to wait !
O sin that hath no equal
  So fast to bar the gate !

O JESU, Thou art pleading
  In accents meek and low,
" I died for you, My children,
  And will ye treat Me so ? "
O LORD, with shame and sorrow
  We open now the door :
Dear SAVIOUR, enter, enter,
  And leave us nevermore.

        BP. W. WALSHAM HOW, 1823-1897.

202

(From the English Hymnal, by permission of the Oxford University Press.)

O LITTLE town of Bethlehem,
  How still we see thee lie !
Above thy deep and dreamless sleep
  The silent stars go by.
Yet in thy dark streets shineth
  The everlasting light ;
The hopes and fears of all the years
  Are met in thee to-night.

How silently, how silently,
  The wondrous gift is given !
So GOD imparts to human hearts
  The blessings of His heaven.
No ear may hear His coming ;
  But in this world of sin,
Where meek souls will receive Him, still
  The dear CHRIST enters in.

O morning stars, together
  Proclaim the holy birth,
And praises sing to GOD the King,
  And peace to men on earth ;
For CHRIST is born of Mary ;
  And, gathered all above,
While mortals sleep, the angels keep
  Their watch of wondering love.

Where children pure and happy
  Pray to the blessèd Child,
Where misery cries out to Thee,
  Son of the mother mild ;
Where charity stands watching
  And faith holds wide the door,
The dark night wakes, the glory breaks,
  And Christmas comes once more.

BP. PHILLIPS BROOKS, 1835-1893

LAUDATE DOMINUM. 5.5.5.5.6.5.6.5. SIR H. PARRY.

(By permission of Novello & Co., Ltd.)

O PRAISE ye the LORD !
  Praise Him in the height ;
Rejoice in His Word,
  Ye Angels of light ;
Ye heavens, adore Him
  By Whom ye were made,
And worship before Him,
  In brightness array'd.

O praise ye the LORD !
  Praise Him upon earth,
In tuneful accord,
  Ye sons of new birth ;
Praise Him Who hath brought you
  His grace from above,
Praise Him Who hath taught you
  To sing of His love.

O praise ye the LORD,
  All things that give sound ;
Each jubilant chord,
  Re-echo around ;
Loud organs, His glory
  Forth tell in deep tone,
And sweet harp, the story
  Of what He hath done.

O praise ye the LORD !
  Thanksgiving and song
To Him be outpour'd
  All ages along :
For love in creation,
  For heaven restored,
For grace of salvation
  O praise ye the LORD !

W. H. BAKER, 1875.

204

O SACRED Head, sore wounded,
  Defiled and put to scorn ;
O kingly Head, surrounded
  With mocking crown of thorn :
What sorrow mars Thy grandeur ?
  Can death Thy bloom deflower ?
O Countenance whose splendour
  The hosts of heaven adore.

Thy beauty, long-desirèd,
  Hath vanished from our sight ;
Thy power is all expirèd,
  And quenched the light of light.
Ah me ! for whom Thou diest,
  Hide not so far Thy grace :
Show me, O Love most highest,
  The brightness of Thy Face.

I pray Thee, JESUS, own me,
  Me, Shepherd good, for Thine ;
Who to Thy fold hast won me,
  And fed with truth divine.
Me guilty, me refuse not,
  Incline Thy Face to me,
This comfort that I lose not,
  On earth to comfort Thee.

In Thy most bitter passion
  My heart to share doth cry,
With Thee for my salvation
  Upon the Cross to die.
Ah, keep my heart thus movèd
  To stand Thy Cross beneath,
To mourn Thee, well-belovèd,
  Yet thank Thee for Thy death.

My days are few, O fail not,
  With Thine immortal power,
To hold me that I quail not
  In death's most fearful hour :
That I may fight befriended,
  And see in my last strife
To me Thine Arms extended
  Upon the Cross of life.

P. GERHARDT, 1607-76
Tr. Y. H.

205

O Sacred Heart.   IRREGULAR.   Laurence Ampleforth.

(By permission of Burns Oates & Washbourne.)

O SACRED Heart !
Our home lies deep in Thee :
   On earth Thou art an exile's rest,
In heav'n the glory of the blest,
   O sacred Heart !

O sacred Heart !
Thou fount of contrite tears,
   Where'er those living waters flow,
New life to sinners they bestow,
   O sacred Heart !

O sacred Heart !
Our trust is all in Thee ;
   For though earth's night be dark and drear,
Thou breathest rest where Thou art near,
   O sacred Heart !

O sacred Heart !
When shades of death shall fall,
   Receive us 'neath Thy gentle care,
And save us from the tempter's snare,
   O sacred Heart !

O sacred Heart !
Lead exiled children home,
   Where we may ever rest near Thee,
In peace and joy eternally,
   O sacred Heart !

                  Fr. Stanfield.

206

Irby.
Unison.

8.7.8.7.7.7.

H. J. Gauntlett, 1805-1876.

Once in royal David's city
  Stood a lowly cattle shed,
Where a Mother laid her Baby
  In a manger for His bed :
Mary was that Mother mild,
Jesus Christ her little Child.

He came down to earth from heaven,
  Who is God and Lord of all,
And His shelter was a stable,
  And His cradle was a stall ;
With the poor, and mean, and lowly,
Lived on earth our Saviour holy.

And through all His wondrous childhood
  He would honour and obey,
Love, and watch the lowly Maiden,
  In whose gentle arms He lay ;
Christian children all must be
Mild, obedient, good as He.

For He is our childhood's pattern,
  Day by day like us He grew,
He was little, weak, and helpless,
  Tears and smiles like us He knew ;
And He feeleth for our sadness,
And He shareth in our gladness.

And our eyes at last shall see Him,
  Through His own redeeming love,
For that Child so dear and gentle
  Is our Lord in heaven above ;
And He leads His children on
To the place where He is gone.

Not in that poor lowly stable,
  With the oxen standing by,
We shall see Him ; but in heaven,
  Set at God's right hand on high ;
When like stars His children crowned
All in white shall wait around.

C. F. Alexander, 1823-95.

LEEDS.
Unison.

6.5.6.5.D.

DUDLEY J. HILL, 1933.

PRAISE we now the Father
  For the mercies sent
Through the SON Incarnate
  In each Sacrament ;
For the pledge and symbol,
  For the outward sign,
For the Grace internal,
  JESU'S Life Divine.

From the days of Abel
  Sacrifice abides ;
As foretold by Abraham,
  GOD Himself provides.
Taught by GOD, we offer
  Firstling of His own,
CHRIST the Sole-begotten
  At the Altar-Throne.

Praise the LORD, ye offspring
  Of a fallen race,
At the Font admitted
  To the means of Grace ;
Born again of water
  And the Holy Dove,
GOD'S own children, folded
  With the Saints above.

Praise the LORD, ye sinners,
  Soiled, from GOD apart ;
Prodigals returning
  With repentant heart ;
For the Absolution
  Gives from sin release,
And the word of pardon
  Bids us go in peace.

Lies the world in darkness,
  Truth from it concealed ;
We in brightness journey,
  By the Spirit sealed ;
Day by day increasing
  In His Gift of Might,
In His Gift of Counsel,
  In His Gift of Sight.

For the Holy Order,
  For the Marriage Tie,
For the Holy Unction
  When about to die,
For such royal birthright,
  HOLY GHOST, to Thee,
CHRIST, with GOD the FATHER
  Glory ever be.

Praise the LORD, ye dying ;
  CHRIST the Vine supplies
To engrafted branches
  Sap which never dies.
Death and Life within us
  Wage their daily strife ;
Those who feed on JESUS
  Have eternal Life.

Praise we then the FATHER
  For the mercies sent
Through the SON Incarnate
  In each Sacrament ;
For the pledge and symbol,
  For the outward sign,
For the Grace internal,
  JESU'S Life Divine.

A. G. G. ROSS.

249

208

BAVARIA.

6.6.6.6.

ANON.
Harmonised by F. E. B.

Unison. Broadly.

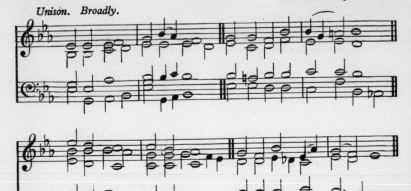

I.

Songs of praise
Now we raise,
God our Lord adoring;
Though in fear,
Gathered here,
Grace and peace imploring.

Throned on high
Thou art nigh,
Nor Thy people failest;
Here Thine own
Altar-Throne
Wondrously unveilest.

His same Voice
Made rejoice
Man in Eden's garden,
Seers of old
Heard and told,
Hope of peace and pardon.

Therefore we
Give to Thee
Glory, praise, and blessing;
Father, Son,
Spirit, One
God in Three confessing.

II.

God's dread Word
First was heard
At the deep's upheaval;
Darkness fled,
Light was shed
O'er the void primeval.

Ages passed;
Then at last
Here the spell was broken;
And men heard
God's same Word
In their own tongue spoken.

Word of Might,
Grant us light,
On Thy mercy leaning,
To discern,
Here to learn
All Thy Gospel's meaning.

ANON.

209

SWEET SACRAMENT DIVINE. IRREGULAR. FR. STANFIELD.

SWEET Sacrament divine !
　Hid in Thine earthly home,
Lo ! round Thy lowly shrine,
　With suppliant hearts we come.
Jesus, to Thee our voice we raise,
In songs of love and heartfelt praise,
　Sweet Sacrament divine !

Sweet Sacrament of Rest !
　Ark from the ocean's roar,
Within Thy shelter blest
　Soon may we reach the shore.
Save us, for still the tempest raves ;
Save, lest we sink beneath the waves ;
　Sweet Sacrament of Rest !

Sweet Sacrament of Peace !
　Dear home for every heart,
Where restless yearnings cease,
　And sorrows all depart.
There in Thine ear, all trustfully
We tell our tale of misery,
　Sweet Sacrament of Peace !

Sweet Sacrament divine !
　Earth's Light and Jubilee,
In Thy clear depths doth shine
　Thy Godhead's Majesty.
Sweet Light, so shine on us, we pray,
That earthly joys may fade away,
　Sweet Sacrament divine !

FR. STANFIELD.

210

GRESHAM.
Unison.

7.6.8.6.D.

GEOFFREY SHAW.

TEN thousand times ten thousand,
In sparkling raiment bright,
The armies of the ransomed Saints
Throng up the steeps of light ;
'Tis finished ! all is finished,
Their fight with death and sin ;
Fling open wide the golden gates,
And let the victors in.

What rush of Alleluyas
Fills all the earth and sky !
What ringing of a thousand harps
Bespeaks the triumph nigh !
O day, for which creation
And all its tribes were made !
O joy, for all its former woes
A thousandfold repaid !

O, then what raptured greetings
On Canaan's happy shore,
What knitting severed friendships up,
Where partings are no more !
Then eyes with joy shall sparkle
That brimmed with tears of late ;
Orphans no longer fatherless,
Nor widows desolate.

Bring near Thy great salvation,
Thou Lamb for sinners slain,
Fill up the roll of Thine elect,
Then take Thy power and reign :
Appear, Desire of Nations ;
Thine exiles long for home ;
Show in the heaven Thy promised sign ;
Thou Prince and SAVIOUR, come.

H. ALFORD, 1810-1871.

211

St. Venantius. *In Unison.* L.M. *Rouen Church Melody.*

A - - men

I.

The God, Whom earth, and sea, and sky
Adore, and laud, and magnify,
Who governs all the threefold frame,
To birth as Child of Mary came.

The Lord, Whom sun and moon obey,
Whom all things serve from day to day,
Was by the Holy Ghost conceived
Of her who through His grace believed.

O blessèd Mother, blessèd Maid,
Thou art the ark wherein was laid
The high Artificer Whose Hand
The round world in its hollow spann'd.

Bless'd in the word that Gabriel brought,
The Holy Ghost within her wrought
To fashion for a human birth
The long Desired of all the earth.

II.

O glorious Maid, exalted far
Beyond the light of burning star,
From Him Who made thee thou hast won
Grace to be Mother of His Son.

All that was lost by woeful Eve
Thy beauteous Offspring did retrieve;
That mourners might regain the height,
Heav'n made of thee its window bright.

Thou wast the great King's entrance door,
Light's gate, through which the sunbeams [pou
Ye ransom'd nations, hail with mirth
Life through the Virgin brought to earth.

All honour, laud, and glory be
O Jesu, Virgin-born to Thee;
All glory, as is ever meet,
To Father and to Paraclete. Amen.

9th Cent., Tr. J. M. Neale.

212

8.7.8.7. B. LUARD SELBY.

(Or 89, *First Tune.*)

(*Copyright* 1904, *by the Proprietors of Hymns A. & M.*)

THE King of love my Shepherd is,
　　Whose goodness faileth never ;
I nothing lack if I am His
　　And He is mine for ever.

Where streams of living water flow
　　My ransom'd soul He leadeth,
And where the verdant pastures grow
　　With food celestial feedeth.

Perverse and foolish oft I stray'd,
　　But yet in love He sought me,
And on His shoulder gently laid,
　　And home, rejoicing, brought me.

Thou spread'st a table in my sight ;
　　Thine unction grace bestoweth ;
And oh, what transport of delight
　　From Thy pure chalice floweth !

In death's dark vale I fear no ill
　　With Thee, dear LORD, beside me ;
Thy rod and staff my comfort still,
　　Thy Cross before to guide me.

And so through all the length of days
　　Thy goodness faileth never ;
Good Shepherd, may I sing Thy praise
　　Within Thy house for ever.

H. W. BAKER, 1821-77.

213

7.6.7.6.D.

B. TOURS.

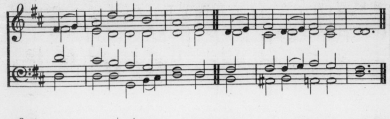

(By permission of Messrs. Novello & Co. Ltd.)

THE Saints of God went forward ;
 Though rough the road they trod,
They neither feared nor faltered
 Because it led to GOD.
Their Father's heavenly city
 Gleamed at the journey's end,
And JESUS went beside them,
 The pilgrim's trusted Friend.

God's children still go forward,
 The way is still the same,
And JESUS calls His servants
 To battle for His name :
To join with holy Alban,
 With Aidan, Bede, and Chad,
To make this land of England,
 A happy land, and glad.

From heaven the Saints are watching ;
 They hold out helping hands
To guide us where GOD's city,
 The golden city, stands.
O JESUS, SAVIOUR, help us
 To win the crowns they won,
That we at last in heaven
 May hear, with them, " Well done."   F. C. BOND.

214

VICTORY.   8.8.8.4.   G. P. DA PALESTRINA, d. 1594.

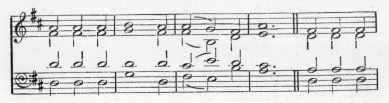

THE strife is o'er, the battle done ;
Now is the Victor's triumph won ;
O let the song of praise be sung :
    Alleluia !

Death's mightiest powers have done their worst,
And JESUS hath His foes dispersed ;
Let shouts of praise and joy outburst ·

On the third morn He rose again
Glorious in majesty to reign ;
O let us swell the joyful strain :

He brake the age-bound chains of hell ;
The bars from heaven's high portals fell ;
Let hymns of praise His triumph tell :

LORD, by the stripes which wounded Thee
From death's dread sting Thy servants free,
That we may live, and sing to Thee.

       18th Cent. *Tr.* F. P.

215

ADORO TE DEVOTE.   10.10.10.10.   MODE V.

(Or Tune 39.)

Thee we adore, O hidden SAVIOUR, Thee,
Who in Thy Sacrament art pleased to be ;
Both flesh and spirit in Thy Presence fail,
Yet here Thy Presence we devoutly hail.

O blest Memorial of our dying LORD,
Who living Bread to men doth here afford !
O may our souls for ever feed on Thee,
And Thou, O CHRIST, for ever precious be.

Fountain of goodness, JESU, LORD and GOD,
Cleanse us, unclean, with Thy most cleansing Blood;
Increase our faith and love, that we may know
The hope and peace which from Thy Presence flow.

O CHRIST, Whom now beneath a veil we see,
May what we thirst for soon our portion be,
To gaze on Thee unveiled, and see Thy Face,
The vision of Thy glory and Thy grace.

AMEN.

S. THOMAS AQUINAS, 1227-1274.

Tr. BP. WOODFORD.

216

C.M. *Melody from " A Collection of Hymns and Sacred Poems," Dublin,* 1749.

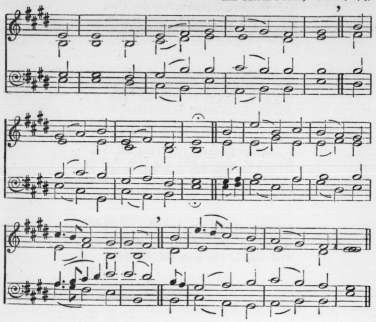

THY kingdom come ! on bended knee
　The passing ages pray ;
And faithful souls have yearned to see
　On earth that kingdom's day.

But the slow watches of the night
　Not less to GOD belong ;
And for the everlasting right
　The silent stars are strong.

And lo, already on the hills
　The flags of dawn appear ;
Gird up your loins, ye prophet souls,
　Proclaim the day is near :

The day in whose clear-shining light
　All wrong shall stand revealed,
When justice shall be throned in might,
　And every heart be healed ;

When knowledge, hand in hand with peace,
　Shall walk the earth abroad ;—
The day of perfect righteousness,
　The promised day of GOD.
　　　　　　　F. L. HOSMER, 1840-1929.

217

Bede.   8.8.7.7.   W. H. Monk.

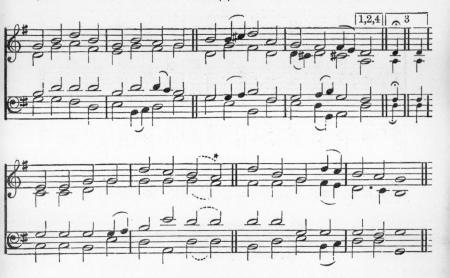

(Or Tune 193.)

(By permission of the Proprietors of Hymns A. & M.)
(* In vv. 2 and 3 this note belongs to the first word of line 4.)

Virgin-born, we bow before Thee ;
Blessèd was the womb that bore Thee ;
Mary, Mother meek and mild,
Blessèd was she in her Child.

Blessèd was the breast that fed Thee ;
Blessèd was the hand that led Thee ;
Blessèd was the parent's eye
That watch'd Thy slumbering infancy.

Blessèd she by all creation,
Who brought forth the world's salvation,
Blessèd they—for ever blest,
Who love Thee most and serve Thee best.

Virgin-born, we bow before Thee :
Blessèd was the womb that bore Thee ;
Mary, Mother meek and mild,
Blessèd was she in her Child.

Bishop Heber, 1783-1826.

218

QUAM DILECTA. 6.6.6.6. BISHOP JENNER, 1820-1898.

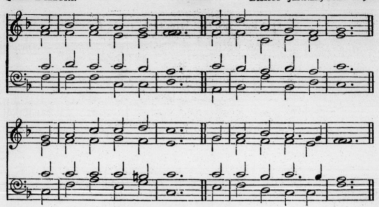

WE love the place, O GOD,
  Wherein Thine honour dwells ;
The joy of Thine abode
  All earthly joy excels.

We love the House of Prayer,
  Wherein Thy servants meet ;
And Thou, O LORD, art there
  Thy chosen flock to greet.

We love the sacred Font,
  For there the Holy Dove
To pour is ever wont
  His blessing from above.

We love Thine Altar, LORD ;
  O, what on earth so dear !
For there, in faith adored,
  We find Thy Presence near.

We love the Word of Life,
  The word that tells of peace,
Of comfort in the strife,
  And joys that never cease.

We love to sing below
  For mercies freely given ;
But O, we long to know
  The triumph-song of heaven !

LORD JESUS, give us grace
  On earth to love Thee more,
In heaven to see Thy Face,
  And with Thy Saints adore.

                W. BULLOCK, 1798-1874.

219

A - - men.

WHEREFORE, O Father, we Thy humble servants
Here bring before Thee CHRIST Thy well-belovèd,
All-perfect Offering, Sacrifice immortal,
        Spotless Oblation.

See now Thy children, making intercession
Through Him our SAVIOUR, SON of GOD incarnate,
For all Thy people, living and departed,
        Pleading before Thee.
                    AMEN.

                      W. H. H. JERVOIS, 1852-1905.

220

WINCHESTER OLD.
(First Tune.)

Este's Psalter, 1592.

NORTHROP.
(Second Tune.)

C.M.

A. NORTHROP (?).

WHILE shepherds watched their flocks by night,
  All seated on the ground,
The Angel of the LORD came down,
  And glory shone around.

" Fear not," said he (for mighty dread
  Had seized their troubled mind);
" Glad tidings of great joy I bring
  To you and all mankind.

" To you in David's town this day
  Is born of David's line
A SAVIOUR, Who is CHRIST the LORD;
  And this shall be the sign :

" The heavenly Babe you there shall find
  To human view displayed,
All meanly wrapped in swathing bands,
  And in a manger laid."

Thus spake the Seraph ; and forthwith
  Appeared a shining throng
Of Angels praising GOD, who thus
  Addressed their joyful song :

" All glory be to God on high,
  And on the earth be peace ;
Good-will henceforth from heaven to men
  Begin and never cease."

NAHUM TATE, 1652-1715.

RENEWAL OF BAPTISMAL VOWS

A MISSION is meant to touch the conscience, to inform the mind, and to direct the will; and all Christian people who come under its influence are invited to renew publicly the promises made at their Baptism. These may be summed up in the words of the Prayer Book:

1. To renounce the devil and all his works, the pomps and vanity of this wicked world, and all the sinful lusts of the flesh.

2. To believe all the articles of the Christian faith.

3. To keep GOD's holy will and commandments, and walk in the same all the days of my life.

Those who are un-baptized or unconfirmed, and those who have neglected the Sacraments should give their names without delay to one of the Missioners, or to the Parish Priest, that they may be duly prepared.

THE MISSION RESOLUTION AND A RULE OF LIFE

ALL who wish the Mission to leave a lasting impression on their lives should make some definite Mission Resolution.

There is no better resolution than to make (or revise) a definite RULE OF LIFE. Experience has proved that it is wise to have a Rule which is simple and which can be kept without great difficulty.

Such a Rule will naturally be based upon the Church's Precepts, and should be made under the following headings:

1. Prayer every morning and night.

2. Attendance at the Lord's Service every Sunday and other Days of Obligation. (N.B.—Worship on Sunday evening also is much to be desired.)

3. Self-examination and Sacramental Confession of sin.

4. Reception of Holy Communion before eating or drinking anything that day.

5. Bible-reading and Meditation.

6. Cheerful and generous Almsgiving.

7. Fasting and Abstinence.

8. Avoiding Temptation.

9. Service for others.

N.B.—It is advisable to ask the advice of the Missioners, or the Parish Priest, before deciding on the details of a Rule of Life.

INDEX OF SUBJECTS

GOD, 27, 32, 41, 70, 83, 93, 94, 108, 123, 191, 197, 200.

Our Lord Jesus Christ:

    Incarnation, 14(1), 16, 87, 177, 202, 206, 220.

    Ministry, 10, 14(1).

    Cross and Passion, 12, 30, 52, 55, 66, 76, 89, 99, 100, 120, 133, 134, 146, 204.

    Resurrection, 62, 67, 68, 214.

    Glorified, 4, 14(2), 34, 130.

God the Holy Spirit, 13, 17, 19, 42, 68, 122, 182.

Invitation, 7, 20, 35, 37, 45, 54, 61, 72, 88, 117, 121, 143, 178.

Sin and Repentance, 2, 23, 31, 45, 79, 82, 105, 117, 135, 144, 156.

Self-Surrender, 46, 47, 126, 136, 201.

Trust in God, 27, 36, 47, 58, 64, 66, 94, 107, 115, 145, 147, 183, 188, 198.

Love of God for man, 36, 55, 98, 127.

Love for Christ, 44, 59, 60, 75, 195, 205, 212.

Response to God's Call, 48, 49, 53, 63, 71, 98, 133, 138.

The Church, 29, 42, 128, 129, 141, 185.

Worship, 1, 18, 32, 41, 218.

The Sacraments, 4, 6, 15, 16, 25, 39, 50, 57, 65, 74, 102, 106, 139, 165, 207, 208, 209, 215, 219.

Praise and Thanksgiving, 81, 92, 108, 109, 123, 147, 150, 187, 199, 203.

Christian Warfare, 24, 26, 38, 40, 86, 104, 110, 118, 132, 140, 150, 154.

Service and the Kingdom, 21, 28, 80, 81, 89, 110, 112, 113, 119, 128, 181, 194, 216.

The Social Order, 70, 83, 93, 103, 119, 142, 184.

Witness, 9, 80, 89, 110, 124, 150.

Perseverance, 24, 38, 85, 95, 111.

Death and Judgment, 33, 67, 77, 79.

The Faithful Departed, 137, 179.

Heaven, 22, 43, 56(1), 152.

Saints and Angels, 8, 11, 43, 56(2), 116, 131, 132, 148, 152, 153, 180, 186, 189, 190, 210, 211, 213, 217.

The Christian Home, 96.

Children, 3, 8, 11, 22, 51, 55, 97, 127, 131, 134, 149, 155, 160, 161, 162, 176, 192, 193, 196, 206.

Processions, 14, 16, 56, 76, 104, 141, 180, 185, 186, 207, 213.

Suitable for Out-of-doors, 7, 58, 73, 88, 94, 104, 112, 125, 140.

Various Prayers and Aspirations, 5, 68, 69, 73, 78, 84, 90, 91, 101, 113, 125.

METRICAL INDEX

S.M.

C.M.

First Line of Hymn.	No.	Name of Tune and Metre.
All hail the power of Jesus' name	1	Miles Lane (C.M.).
All my sins uprising now	2	Nicht so Traurig (7.7.7.7.7.7.).
All we have we owe to Jesus	3	1. Shipston (8.7.8.7.). 2. Rosettenville (8.7.8.7.).
Alleluia, sing to Jesus	4	Hillingdon (8.7.8.7.D.).
Almighty God, Whose only Son	5	Melcombe (L.M.).
And now, O Father, mindful of the love ...	6	Unde et memores (10.10.10.10.10.10.).
Art thou weary, art thou languid	7	Art Thou Weary (8.5.8.3.).
Around the throne of God a band ...	8	Solothurn (L.M.).
Ashamed of Thee, O dearest Lord ...	9	Wareham (L.M.).
At even ere the sun was set	10	Angelus (L.M.).
Ave Maria! Blessèd Maid!...	11	St. Alban (8.8.6.D.).
Beneath the Cross of Jesus	12	Beneath the Cross (IRREGULAR).
Breathe on me, Breath of God	13	Trentham (S.M.).
Christ from heaven descended	14	Ballo di Manova (IRREGULAR).
Christ is the Sacrifice we plead	15	1. St. Deiniol (D.C.M. and Refrain). 2. Gosterwood (D.C.M. and Refrain).
Christians, sing the Incarnation	16	Soldiers of the Church (8.7.8.7.D. with Refrain).
Come, Holy Ghost, our souls inspire ...	17	Veni Creator (L.M.).
Come let us sing the song of songs ...	18	Warrington (L.M.).
Come, Thou Holy Spirit, come	19	Veni Sancte Spiritus (7.7.7.7.7.7.).
Come, ye sinners, poor and needy ...	20	Mannheim (8.7.8.7.8.7.).
Come ye yourselves apart	21	St. Agnes (10.10.10.10.).
Daily, daily, sing the praises	22	Daily, daily (8.7.8.7.D.).
Depth of mercy, can there be	23	Nun Komm, der Heiden Heiland (7.7.7.7.).
Faithful warriors, bearing	24	1. Warfare (6.5.6.5.). 2. Victors (6.5.6.5.D.).
Father, Who dost Thy children feed ...	25	Stella (8.8.8.8.8.8.).
Fight the good fight with all thy might ...	26	Duke Street (L.M.).
Firmly I believe and truly	27	Stafford (8.7.8.7.).
From the depths of sin and failure ...	28	Ebenezer (Ton-y-Botel) (8.7.8.7.D.).
Glorious things of thee are spoken ...	29	Austria (8.7.8.7.D.).
Glory be to Jesus	30	1. Glory be to Jesus (6.5.6.5.D. and Refrain). 2. Caswall (6.5.6.5.).
God made me for Himself	31	Eventide (10.10.10.10.).
God of love, and truth, and beauty ...	32	St. Denys (8.5.8.5.8.8.8.5.).
Great God, what do I see and hear ...	33	Luther (8.7.8.7.8.8.7.).
Hail the day that sees Him rise	34	Llanfair (7.4.7.4.D.).
Hark a sweet voice calleth	35	La Meuniere (IRREGULAR).
Hark, my soul! it is the Lord	36	St. Bees (7.7.7.7.).
He is pleading, by His sorrows	37	Pleading Saviour (8.7.8.7.D.).
He who would valiant be	38	Monks Gate (11.11.12.11.).
Here, O my Lord, I see Thee face to face	39	Ellers (10.10.10.10.).
Ho, my comrades! see the signal	40	Hold the fort (IRREGULAR).
Holy, Holy, Holy! Lord God Almighty ...	41	Nicaea (11.12.12.10.).
Holy Spirit ever dwelling	42	Deerhurst (8.7.8.7.D.).
How bright these glorious spirits shine! ...	43	Bromsgrove (C.M.).

First Line of Hymn.	No.	Name of Tune and Metre.
How sweet the Name of Jesus sounds ...	44	1. St. Peter (C.M.). 2. Holy Name (C.M. and Refrain).
Hush, my soul, what Voice is pleading? ...	45	Evensong (8.7.8.7.D.).
I am Thine, O Lord, I have heard ...	46	Convention (IRREGULAR).
I am trusting Thee, Lord Jesus	47	Bullinger (8.5.8.3.).
I hear Thy welcome Voice	48	I hear Thy welcome (IRREG.).
I heard the Voice of Jesus say	49	Kingsfold (D.C.M.).
I hunger and I thirst	50	Eccles (6.6.6.6.).
I love to hear the story	51	I Love to Hear the Story (7.6.7.6.D. and Refrain).
I met the Good Shepherd	52	The Good Shepherd (11.11.11.11.).
I need Thee ev'ry hour	53	Dependence (IRREGULAR).
In the land of strangers	54	Far Land (IRREGULAR).
It is a thing most wonderful	55	Herongate (L.M.).
Jerusalem, my happy home	56	1. Jerusalem (C.M.). 2. St. Austin (C.M.).
Jesu, gentlest Saviour	57	1. Fulstow (6.5.6.5.). 2. Monod (6.5.6.5.).
Jesu, Lover of my soul	58	Hollingside (7.7.7.7.D.).
Jesu, my Lord, my God, my All	59	1. Surrey (8.8.8.8.8.8.). 2. St. Catherine (8.8.8.8.8.8.).
Jesus! Refuge of the weary	60	Ad Inferos (8.7.8.7.).
Jesus calls us o'er the tumult	61	Merton (8.7.8.7.).
Jesus Christ is risen to-day	62	Easter Hymn (7.4.7.4.D.).
Jesus, I my cross have taken	63	St. Oswald (8.7.8.7.).
Jesus, I will trust Thee	64	Goshen (6.5.6.5.D.).
Jesus, in Thy dear Sacrament	65	Corpus Christi (C.M.).
Jesus, keep me near the Cross	66	Near the cross (IRREGULAR).
Jesus lives! thy terrors now	67	St. Albinus (7.8.7.8.4.).
Jesus stand among us	68	St. Ninian (6.5.6.5.).
Jesus! speak to me in love	69	Dismissal (7.7.7.7.7.7.).
Judge eternal, throned in splendour ...	70	Rhuddlan (8.7.8.7.8.7.).
Just as I am, without one plea	71	Saffron Walden (8.8.8.6.).
Knocking, knocking, who is there? ...	72	Knocking (IRREGULAR).
Lead, kindly light, amid the encircling ...	73	1. Lux Benigna (10.4.10.4.10.10.). 2. Sandon (10.4.10.4.10.10.).
Let all mortal flesh keep silence	74	Picardy (8.7.8.7.8.7.).
Let me come closer to Thee, Jesus ...	75	1. Father Henry (9.6.9.6.). 2. Ignatius (9.6.9.6.).
Lift high the Cross, the love of Christ ...	76	Crucifer (10.10. and Refrain).
Lo! He comes with clouds descending ...	77	Helmsley (8.7.8.7.4.7.).
Lord, I hear of showers of blessing ...	78	Even me (8.7.8.7.6.7.).
Lord, in this Thy mercy's day	79	St. Philip (7.7.7.).
Lord, speak to me, that I may speak ...	80	Holley (L.M.).
Lord, Thy ransomed Church is waking ...	81	Alleluia (8.7.8.7.D.).
Low, at Thy pierced feet	82	Humility (IRREGULAR).
Mine eyes have seen the glory	83	Mine eyes have seen (IRREG.).
More holiness give me	84	Irchester (IRREGULAR).
My faith looks up to Thee	85	Olivet (6.6.4.6.6.6.4.).
Narrow thy path, O pilgrim lone	86	Grimaudin (IRREGULAR).
O come, all ye faithful	87	Adeste Fideles (IRREGULAR).
O come to the merciful Saviour	88	Hiding in Thee (IRREGULAR).
O dearest Lord, Thy sacred Brow ...	89	1. St. Columba (C.M.). 2. Divine Compassion (C.M.).
O for a closer walk with God	90	Belmont (C.M.).
O for a heart to praise my God	91	1. Bangor (C.M.). 2. Sawley (C.M.).

First Line of Hymn.	No.	Name of Tune and Metre.
O for a thousand tongues to sing	92	1. Lansdowne (C.M.). 2. Evan (C.M.).
O God of earth and altar	93	Kings Lynn (7.6.7.6.D.).
O God, our help in ages past	94	St. Anne (C.M.).
O Jesus, I have promised	95	Wolvercote (7.6.7.6.D.).
O Jesus, bless our homes	96	Battyeford (6.6.6.6.).
O Jesus ! God and Man	97	Waldegrave (6.8.6.8.).
O love that wilt not let me go	98	St. Margaret (8.8.8.8.6.).
O my Saviour lifted	99	North Coates (6.5.6.5.).
O Soul of Jesus, sick to death ...	100	Hesperus (L.M.).
O Thou Who makest souls to shine ...	101	Hereford (L.M.).
Once, only once, and once for all ...	102	Stracathro (C.M.).
Once to every man and nation	103	Hyfrydol (8.7.8.7.D.).
Onward, Christian soldiers	104	St. Gertrude (6.5.6.5.D. and Refrain).
Pass me not, O gentle Saviour	105	Pass me not (IRREGULAR).
Peace, peace, Jesus is here	106	Peace, Peace (IRREGULAR).
Peace, perfect peace	107	Song 46 (10.10.).
Praise, my soul, the King of heaven ...	108	Praise, my soul (8.7.8.7.8.7.).
Praise to the Holiest in the height ...	109	1. Hebdomadal (C.M.). 2. Gerontius (C.M.).
" Quit you like men," life's battle ...	110	Angels of Jesus (IRREGULAR).
Redeemed, restored, forgiven	111	Merionydd (7.6.7.6.D.).
Rescue the perishing	112	Roslynlee (IRREGULAR).
Revive Thy work, O Lord	113	St. Thomas (S.M.).
Rock of ages, cleft for me	114	Rock of Ages (7.7.7.7.7.7.).
Safe in the arms of Jesus	115	Safe in the Arms of Jesus (7.6.7.6.D. and Refrain).
Shall we not love thee, Mother dear ...	116	1. Bishopthorpe (C.M.). 2. Shall we not love Thee (C.M. and Refrain).
Sinners, turn, why will ye die	117	Ives (7.7.7.7.D.).
Soldiers of Christ, arise	118	1. From Strength to Strength. (D.S.M.). 2. St. Ethelwald (S.M.).
Son of God, eternal Saviour	119	Rustington (8.7.8.7.D.).
Soul of Jesus, make me whole	120	Aberystwyth (7.7.7.7.D.).
Souls of men, why will ye scatter ...	121	1. Animae hominum (8.7.8.7.). 2. Llansannan (8.7.8.7.D.).
Spirit Divine, attend our prayers ...	122	Ilfracombe (C.M.).
Stand up and bless the Lord	123	1. Carlisle (S.M.). 2. Huddersfield (S.M.).
Stand up ! stand up for Jesus	124	1. Morning Light (7.6.7.6.D.). 2. Stand up for Jesus (7.6.7.6.D. and Refrain)
Sun of my soul, Thou Saviour dear ...	125	1. Birling (L.M.). 2. Hursley (L.M.).
Take my life and let it be	126	Dedication (7.7.7.7.).
Tell me the old, old story	127	The old, old story (7.6.7.6.D. and Refrain).
The Church of God a kingdom is	128	University (C.M.).
The Church's one foundation	129	Aurelia (7.6.7.6.D.).
The Head that once was crowned	130	St. Magnus (Nottingham) (C.M.).
The saints all crowned with glory ...	131	Skerton (7.6.7.6.D.).
The Son of God goes forth to war ...	132	Richmond (C.M.).
There is a fountain filled with blood ...	133	Wiltshire (C.M.).
There is a green hill far away	134	1. Horsley (C.M.). 2. Love Divine (C.M. and Refrain).

First Line of Hymn.	No.	Name of Tune and Metre.
There were ninety and nine	135	The Ninety and Nine (IRREG.).
Thine for ever, God of love	136	Newington (7.7.7.7.).
Think, O Lord, in mercy	137	Corpus Domini (6.5.6.5.D.).
Thou didst leave Thy throne	138	Margaret (IRREGULAR).
Thou, Who at Thy first Eucharist ...	139	Sacramentum Unitatis (10.10.10.10.10.10.).
Through the night of doubt and sorrow ...	140	Marching (8.7.8.7.).
Thy Hand, O God, has guided	141	Thornbury (7.6.7.6.D.).
Thy kingdom come, O God	142	St. Cecilia (6.6.6.6.).
To-day Thy mercy calls us	143	Missionary Hymn (7.6.7.6.D.).
Weary of earth and laden with my sin ...	144	Dalkeith (10.10.10.10.).
What a Friend we have in Jesus ...	145	Chislehurst (8.7.8.7.D.).
When I survey the wondrous Cross ...	146	Rockingham (L.M.).
When upon life's billows	147	Count your blessings (IRREG.).
Who are these like stars appearing ...	148	All Saints (8.7.8.7.7.7.).
Who is He in yonder stall ?	149	Resonet in Laudibus (IRREG.).
Who is on the Lord's side ?	150	Hermas (6.5.6.5.D. and Refrain).
With harps and with viols	151	Viols (11.12. and Refrain).
Ye watchers and ye holy ones	152	Lasst uns erfreuen (8.8.4.4.8.8. and Alleluias).
Ye who own the faith of Jesus ...	153	St. Barnabas Oxford (8.7.8.7.D.)
Yield not to temptation	154	Fortitude (IRREGULAR).

LITANIES.

Litany of the Holy Childhood	155	London Town (7.7.7.6.).
Litany of Penitence	156	Litany A. (11.10.11.7.).
Litany of Intercession	157	St. Mark (7.7.7.6.).

ACTS OF DEVOTION, ETC.

God be in my head	158	Poplar.
The End of Man	159	Anon.
A Rule of Life (for Children)	160	
Act of Faith, Hope and Love (for Children)	161	
Act of Contrition	162	
A Prayer of St. Richard of Chichester ...	163	
Benedictus and Agnus Dei	164	
O Salutaris	165(I)	Verbum Supernum Prodiens (L.M.).
Tantum Ergo	165(II)	1. St. Audrey (8.7.8.7.8.7.). 2. Tantum ergo (8.7.8.7.8.7.). 3. Benediction (8.7.8.7.8.7.).
O Saviour of the world, etc.	166	
Anima Christi	167	
Acts of Faith, etc.	168	
Psalm 51	169	
Psalm 130	170	
Psalm 103	171	
Psalm 150	172	
Te Deum	173	
Magnificat	174	
Nunc Dimittis	175	

First Line of Hymn.	No.	Name of Tune and Metre.
Advent tells us Christ is near	176	Keine Schonheit hat die Welt (7.7.7.7.).
As with gladness men of old	177	Dix (7.7.7.7.7.7.).
Cast thy care on Jesus	178	Cranham (6.5.6.5.D.).
Christ enthroned in highest heaven ...	179	St. Thomas (8.7.8.7.8.7.).
Christ the fair glory of the holy Angels ...	180	Coelites Plaudant (11.11.11.5.).
City of God, how broad and far	181	Richmond (C.M.).
Come down, O Love Divine	182	Down Ampney (6.6.11.D.).
Come Thou long expected Jesus ...	183	St. Andrew (8.7.8.7.).
Eternal Father, strong to save	184	Melita (8.8.8.8.8.8.).
Faith of our fathers, taught of old ...	185	Psalm 68 (8.8.7.8.8.7.D.).
For all the Saints	186	Sine Nomine (10.10.10.4.).
Glory to Jesus	187	Bunessan (IRREGULAR).
Guide me, O Thou great Redeemer ...	188	Caersalem (8.7.8.7.4.7.).
Hail, O Star that pointest	189	Ave Maris Stella (6.6.6.6.).
He, whose confession God of old accepted	190	Iste Confessor (11.11.11.5.).
Immortal, invisible, God only wise ...	191	St. Denio (11.11.11.11.).
Jesus Divine	192	Dear Child Divine(8.6.8.6.8.6,).
Jesu, good above all other	193	Quem Pastores laudavere (8.8.8.7.).
Jesus shall reign where'er the sun ...	194	Truro (L.M.).
Jesus, these eyes have never seen ...	195	Nun danket all (C.M.).
Lo ! round the throne a glorious band ...	196	Rex gloriose Martyrum (L.M.).
My God, how wonderful Thou art ...	197	Westminster (C.M.).
Nearer, my God, to Thee	198	{ 1. Rothwell (6.4.6.4.6.6.4.). 2. Horbury (6.4.6.4.6.6.4.).
Now thank we all our God	199	Nun danket (6.7.6.7.6.6.6.6.).
O blest Creator of the light	200	Lucis Creator (L.M.).
O Jesu, Thou art standing	201	St. Catherine (7.6.7.6.D.).
O little town of Bethlehem	202	Forest Green (D.C.M.).
O praise ye the Lord !	203	Laudate Dominum (5.5.5.5.6.5.6.5.).
O Sacred Head, sore wounded	204	Passion Chorale (7.6.7.6.D.).
O Sacred Heart !	205	O Sacred Heart (IRREGULAR).
Once in royal David's city	206	Irby (8.7.8.7.7.7.).
Praise we now the Father	207	Leeds (6.5.6.5.D.).
Songs of praise	208	Bavaria (6.6.6.6.).
Sweet Sacrament Divine	209	Sweet Sacrament Divine (IRREGULAR).
Ten thousand times ten thousand	210	Gresham (7.6.8.6.D.).
The God, Whom earth, and sea, and sky ...	211	St. Venantius (L.M.).
The King of love my Shepherd is	212	Wishford (8.7.8.7.).
The Saints of God went forward	213	Tours (7.6.7.6.D.).
The strife is o'er, the battle done	214	Victory (8.8.8.4.).
Thee we adore, O hidden Saviour, Thee ...	215	Adoro Te devote (10.10.10.10.).
Thy kingdom come ! on bended knee ...	216	Irish (C.M.).
Virgin-born, we bow before Thee	217	Bede (8.8.7.7.).
We love the place, O God	218	Quam Dilecta (6.6.6.6.).
Wherefore,O Father, we Thy humble servants	219	Christe Fons Jugis (11.11.11.5.).
While shepherds watched their flocks by night	220	{ 1. Winchester old (C.M.). 2. Northrop (C.M.).